CW00405810

Contents

Key messages

General practice is in crisis. Workload has increased substantially in recent years and has not been matched by growth in either funding or in workforce. A lack of nationally available, real-time data means that this crisis has been until recently largely invisible to commissioners and policy-makers. Our report provides the most detailed analysis to date about how and why this crisis occurred.

Our analysis of 30 million patient contacts from 177 practices found that consultations grew by more than 15 per cent between 2010/11 and 2014/15. The number of face-to-face consultations grew by 13 per cent and telephone consultations by 63 per cent. Over the same period, the GP workforce grew by 4.75 per cent and the practice nurse workforce by 2.85 per cent. Funding for primary care as a share of the NHS overall budget fell every year in our five-year study period, from 8.3 per cent to just over 7.9 per cent.

Pressures on general practice are compounded by the fact that the work is becoming more complex and more intense. This is mainly because of the ageing population, increasing numbers of people with complex conditions, initiatives to move care from hospitals to the community, and rising public expectations. Surveys show that GPs in the NHS report finding their job more stressful than their counterparts in other countries.

Practices are finding it increasingly difficult to recruit and retain GPs. GPs reaching the end of their careers are choosing to retire early in response to workload pressures. They have also been affected by changes to the tax treatment of pensions which create disincentives to work when the lifetime allowance for pensions has been reached.

Fewer GPs are choosing to undertake full-time clinical work with more opting for portfolio careers or working part-time. This is true for both male and female GPs. Trainee GPs are often planning to work on a salaried basis. This continues a long-term trend in which fewer doctors aspire to become partners in their practices.

There are challenges too with recruitment and retention of other members of the primary care team particularly practice nurses and practice managers. This makes it difficult for some of the work of GPs to be taken on by other staff who are also in short supply.

As the pressures on general practice have grown, the experience for patients has deteriorated, albeit from high levels. The latest national GP patient survey found that 85 per cent of patients were able to get an appointment to see or speak to someone the last time they tried, down from 87 per cent two years previously. It also showed a reduction in the rating patients gave to their interactions with staff in GP practices.

Our findings point to a service that has traditionally been seen as the jewel in the crown of the NHS coming under growing pressure through a combination of factors. The Department of Health and NHS England have failed over a number of years to collect data that would have provided advance warning of the crisis now facing general practice. Action is urgently needed to reverse reductions in funding as a share of the NHS budget and to recruit and retain the workforce needed to meet rising patient demands.

Securing the future of general practice cannot be achieved simply through more of the same, even though more investment is needed. It requires a willingness to do things differently building on examples of approaches already in development in several areas. The new commitments to support outlined in the *General practice forward view* (NHS England 2016b) will need to be monitored to ensure they can address the urgent crisis. Commissioners and policy-makers must resist the temptation to place additional responsibilities on general practice until additional investment and staff are in place. To avoid the service falling apart, in our view, the immediate priorities are to:

- provide practical support to practices to apply established quality and service improvement techniques

- accelerate the uptake of technologies and ways of working that can help practices deal with growing pressures more effectively, including telephone triage and email consultations where appropriate

- encourage the further development of the primary care workforce not only through the use of nurses, pharmacists and physician associates, but also through new roles such as health coaches and the use of volunteers

- recognise that supporting hard-pressed staff to provide care more effectively is as important as recruiting additional staff to address the growing recruitment crisis

- reduce the bureaucratic burden on practices, for example, from the Care Quality Commission and from the complexities involved in relationships between primary and secondary care

- place general practice at the heart of sustainability and transformation plans to ensure that the voice of general practice is heard and acted on in the system-wide plans being developed for the use of the additional funding provided to the NHS

- support patients to use services appropriately through better signposting and also by making it easy for patients to seek advice not only from GPs but also from the wider primary care team, encouraging access to a wider range of options such as those available through social prescribing.

NHS England should report regularly on progress in implementing the commitments contained in the *General practice forward view*, particularly those related to increases in funding for general practice and in the workforce.

In the longer term:

- NHS England must overcome current deficiencies in data and intelligence that have allowed the current crisis to develop. This includes reporting trends in activity and performance in general practice in a similar way to the reporting of trends in hospital activity and performance

- local health systems should continue to develop new and innovative models of general practice (for example, multispecialty community providers) with a balance struck between the benefits of working at a scale through federations and networks and making sure services are responsive to local people

- new models of general practice must enable GPs or their team members to take on the task of co-ordinating care for their local population, by providing them with the resources in terms of time, money, skill mix and (crucially) closer working relationships with secondary and community care teams

- new voluntary contracts will need to be developed for practices that wish to lead the development of integrated out-of-hospital services which would fund care for a defined population, require practices to link with others to work at scale and be focused on the outcomes they would be expected to deliver

- Health Education England must design a workforce strategy to support more sustainable careers for GPs and their fellow team members, promoting sustainable and fulfilling options for development and recognising changing career preferences among GPs.

These measures are designed to improve the experience of patients and deliver care that is accessible and offers continuity.

Introduction

It seems that hardly a week goes by without a new story in the press about general practice under pressure. Evidence suggests that people are finding it increasingly difficult to get GP appointments; politicians are pressing for extended opening hours; and surveys of GPs report low morale, unmanageable workload and problems with recruitment. These mounting concerns have, in recent months, prompted inquiries by the Health Select Committee, the Public Accounts Committee and the National Audit Office (NAO) into access to general practice.

Surveys show generally high public satisfaction with general practice, and the annual British Social Attitudes (BSA) survey consistently finds it to be the most popular part of the NHS. However, satisfaction levels declined during the previous parliament, from 77 per cent in 2010 to 71 per cent in 2014 (Appleby and Robertson 2015). This trend continued in the most recent survey, falling to 69 per cent – the lowest level since the survey began in 1983 (Appleby and Robertson 2016). The NHS GP patient survey has shown similar trends, revealing high but declining levels of satisfaction with overall experience and in specific areas, particularly access and continuity (Ipsos MORI 2016).

As we went to press with this report, NHS England published its *General practice forward view* (NHS England 2016b) which sets out its immediate actions in response to mounting concerns. But where is the evidence that explains the causes of this pressure on general practice? How many consultations are carried out each week? Do people have more complicated health issues now? Or are people more demanding? The truth is, there is really no way of knowing at the moment. Despite the seemingly vast amounts of data that individual GP practices collect, since 2008 there has been no systematic national data collection that can tell us about the number or nature of consultations, and who undertakes them (National Audit Office 2015). An extrapolation of the 2008 data is still used today by national bodies to estimate growth in the number of consultations nationally (Deloitte 2014). In its 2015 report on access to general practice, the National Audit Office strongly recommended that NHS England improves the data it collects on demand and supply.

Despite the lack of nationally available data, this report attempts to illuminate changes in activity that might explain this feeling of crisis in general practice. It also addresses the lack of available information by using both qualitative and quantitative analysis of new data sources.

What is general practice?

General practice is widely recognised to be the foundation on which NHS care is based. The core purpose of general practice, set out in the national GP contract, is very broadly described as the services that GPs must provide to manage a registered list of patients. This might include consultation, treatment or onward referral for investigation. GPs may also provide extended primary care services, such as prevention, screening, immunisations, and some diagnostic services. GPs also help to ensure effective co-ordination of care for their patients, including with other NHS services, social care and health services outside the NHS.

The majority of GPs work as independent contractors under the terms of a national contract. Two contractual routes account for the majority of spending: the General Medical Services (GMS) contract and the Personal Medical Services (PMS) contract, held by around 56 per cent and 40 per cent of GP practices respectively. Alternative Provider Medical Services (APMS) contracts are used to buy primary care services from GP practices with one of the two main contract types, but also to buy them from other bodies like non-NHS voluntary providers.

In 2014 there were around 37,000 full-time equivalent (FTE) GPs in England, working in around 7,875 practices. GP practice size varies significantly, but the average number of patients per practice has grown steadily in the past few years, from 6,610 to 7,171 between 2010 and 2014, reflecting a move towards larger practices. The number of single-handed practices is now 843 (10.7 per cent) – a 30 per cent fall since 2010. The average number of patients per GP varies depending on the area, but has remained fairly stable over the past five years, rising from 1,567 in 2010 to 1,577 in 2014. The proportion of salaried GPs has increased over time to around 27 per cent; just over half of the GP workforce is female (Health and Social Care Information Centre 2015a).

Methodology

Quantitative analysis

- A study of 30 million individual contacts with patients from 177 practices over five years provided by ResearchOne, the non-profit research arm of TPP, a major supplier of GP information systems.

- A survey of 43 practices for a sample week in October 2015 examining activity and workload.

- A survey of 318 GP trainees, examining workload and future career intentions.

Qualitative analysis

- In-depth semi-structured interviews with 60 staff at four practices of varying sizes in Plymouth, Shrewsbury, Sheffield and London.

- Literature search and analysis.

- Scoping conversations with a range of stakeholders, including national bodies and leaders of clinical commissioning groups (CCGs).

- Qualitative analysis of free text answers from a survey of 318 GP trainees.

Analysis of ResearchOne data

ResearchOne is a health and care research database consisting of pseudonymised clinical and administrative data drawn from the electronic health records of around 6 million patients currently held on TPP's SystmOne. This component of the study was approved by the ResearchOne project committee under the terms of the favourable approval by the National Research Ethics Service, Research Ethics Committee North East (REC reference number 11/NE/0184). The data extract we used for analysis comprises 30 million individual contacts with patients in 177 practices between 2010/11 and 2014/15. It includes:

- staff type(s) conducting the activity

- the form of activity (eg, face-to-face or telephone)

- age of the patient

- number of pre-existing chronic conditions based around the chronic disease register maintained in general practice (for example, chronic obstructive pulmonary disease or diabetes) coded within the patient's SystmOne medical record at the start of the appointment

- number of drugs the patient is currently prescribed

- Index of Multiple Deprivation (IMD) 2010 rank

- the date and start time of each appointment

- the staff role of the person (or people) involved with the contact

- information on additional activity conducted during the appointment, including whether a prescription was generated, vaccines administered or referrals made to other services.

All statistics derived from the ResearchOne data are presented in relative rather than absolute terms, and should be applied only to our sample, rather than England as a whole. Practices in our data extract have an average deprivation rank higher than the national average (mean IMD rank in 2014/15 was ~14,000 and the maximum average rank was 32,482) and the average practice list size is smaller (6,825 registered patients per practice in our sample in 2014/15, compared with 7,171 nationally). These differences in representativeness may be overcome through further statistical modelling, but we were unable to conduct such changes in the time available for our analysis. We have instead focused on the internal validity of our sample.

An issue with the completeness of appointment records in April 2010 and the first half of May 2010 meant that we were unable to include the data from that period in our analysis. In order to obtain a full five-year analysis of activity we have estimated the number of contacts in these two months by using data from 2011/12 until 2014/15 to generate an expected number of each type of contact by staff group. The numbers generated through this technique may represent an overestimate of activity, creating slight overall underestimates of each of the percentage changes in activity over the course of the study period. However, the estimate has been applied to less than 3 per cent of our data, and when checked by creating estimates for months where we do have robust data, there is no statistically significant difference.

It is important to note that SystmOne – like all other general practice information systems – is designed for practices to conduct their everyday work and not for the purpose of secondary use of data for analysis. Unlike secondary care, there are no national standards for data entry about activity in general practice. This means we have had to make certain assumptions about the way some data is coded, as follows.

- Staff type: There are many roles identified within the dataset. Our sub-analysis considers activity for GPs, nurses and 'other' clinical staff groups, which includes health care assistants and paramedics among others. Activity carried out by administrative and non-clinical staff has been excluded from our analysis of workload.

- Form of activity: The main type of activity recorded in the extract was 'face-to-face' or 'telephone'. A wide range of other activity types was recorded, with considerably fewer entries, but we have excluded these from our analysis as there is uncertainty about how they are applied and whether they are applied consistently across practices. ('Bulk operation', for example, accounts for some 0.26 per cent of total activity in 2010/11, but we cannot attribute this to direct patient activity with any confidence and so have excluded it from our analysis. Other examples include 'contact with relative/carer' and 'case conference'.) The proportion of face-to-face contacts relative to the number of telephone consultations is higher than we would anticipate from other work. We suspect this is partly because of the way that appointment booking information is inputted by staff at practices, and in particular that contacts in the patient's home and at care homes are recorded as 'face-to-face' contact as they do not appear in any other form in the data.

- Double-counting: The data extract avoids double-counting of activity within consultations by linking multiple contacts to the same appointment ID. These are counted only once in our analysis in each calculation. Our calculations of the average number of chronic conditions, age and IMD rank of patients are all based on these distinct entries to guard against duplication in these calculations as well.

- Additional contact: Each separate entry with a unique identifier in the appointment ID field of the data is counted as an additional contact if it is a face-to-face or telephone contact conducted with a clinical staff member.

- Per-patient ratios: Where possible, we have included per-patient ratios based on the registered patient list size of the individual practices in the data as well as relative changes in the size of the patient list over time. This is done to give a sense of the change in activity relative to demographic changes in the populations being served by the practices in our sample.

- Appointment length: Although start and end times of appointments were captured, we excluded these fields from our analysis because of the way in which the data was entered. The appointment length of a typical contact in the data appeared to be unrealistically long. Having spoken to staff who use SystmOne, it became clear that they often left the appointment record open until any administrative tasks were completed, even if this was some time after the consultation actually ended.

Workload survey

We advertised for practices to participate in both the survey and the case study site visits through The King's Fund's own networks and through the Clinical Innovation and Research Centre of the Royal College of General Practitioners (RCGP).

We developed a short Excel spreadsheet for self-completion based on the 2007 national GP workload survey, and piloted the tool with a small number of practices. A total of 100 practices volunteered to receive a survey and 43 returned completed surveys for the week beginning 5 October 2015. Data items included staffing levels, clinical activity (for example, telephone consultations, surgery visits, home visits, care home visits, clinics) and non-clinical activity (referrals, governance, management, meetings, etc). The workload survey was completed by 43 practices for a seven-day period in October 2015. The average practice completing this survey was much larger than our ResearchOne sample – on average, 10,800 registered patients. (One practice from Scotland and one from Wales responded but the results on activity were not dissimilar from the other English practices and so we chose to include them in our analysis.)

Case study sites

We selected four of the 100 practices that responded to our initial contact for our qualitative research. We used two variables – practice size and geography – to select the following four practices.

- Beacon Medical Group, Plymouth: Recently formed from the merger of three practices, with a registered patient population of 31,669 and four surgeries stretching from the edge of Plymouth to Dartmoor.

- City Road Medical Centre, Islington: A small inner-city practice with a registered patient population of 6,415, serving a diverse patient population including deprived groups, affluent City workers and a transient student population.

- Page Hall Medical Centre, Sheffield: A practice with a 7,350 registered patient population in a very deprived area, with a high proportion of patients from black and minority ethnic groups and newly arrived migrant communities.

- Riverside Medical Centre, Shrewsbury: A market-town practice with a registered patient population of 10,047.

We developed and piloted a semi-structured interview schedule and interviewed 60 staff in total across the four sites, including GPs, GP trainees, nurses, allied health care professionals, practice managers and reception staff during November and December 2015. These interviews were transcribed and subject to a thematic analysis.

Survey of GP trainees

We surveyed GP trainees across England regarding their career intentions and working patterns. A self-completion questionnaire was designed and piloted with a number of trainees. The survey was distributed to GPs via programme managers taking part in the General Practice Vocational Training Scheme. An online survey tool was used to collect responses. Responses were received from 318 trainees at a range of training stages (ST1–3). We conducted quantitative analysis of multiple choice items from the questionnaire, and thematic analysis of free text answers.

② Activity: has general practice got busier?

There is no routine public reporting of GP activity data and no standardised national dataset. The only data available is extracted for secondary analysis from various GP clinical systems and is therefore subject to similar restrictions and limitations to those we outline in our use of the ResearchOne dataset. An extrapolation of data from QResearch (taken from practices using EMIS clinical information systems) published in 2009 is still used today by national bodies to estimate growth in the number of consultations nationally. This predicted a growth in activity of around 14 per cent between 2010/11 and 2014/15 (Deloitte 2014). A recent National Institute for Health Research (NIHR) funded study using data extracted from the Clinical Practice Research Datalink (CPRD) (taken from practices using the Vision clinical information system) found a 10.5 per cent increase in GP and nurse consultations between 2007 and 2014 (Hobbs *et al* 2016). The Nuffield Trust also reported analysis of CPRD data showing an 11 per cent increase between 2010/11 and 2013/14 (Curry 2015). It is not possible to directly compare findings sourced from different information systems due to the differences in the way activity is coded and recorded by practices using these clinical systems.

Total consultations

The ResearchOne data (*see* Figure 1) revealed that total direct face-to-face and telephone contacts with patients increased by 15.4 per cent across all clinical staff groups between 2010/11 and 2014/15. During the same period, the average patient list size increased by 10 per cent.

Overall consultations per registered patient per year for clinical staff groups rose from 4.29 in 2010/11 to 4.91 in 2014/15.

Our workload survey of 43 practices found wide variation in the average number of contacts with patients, from 0.07 contacts per registered patient to 0.19 contacts. Taken over the course of a year, that would be a range of 3.64 to 9.88.

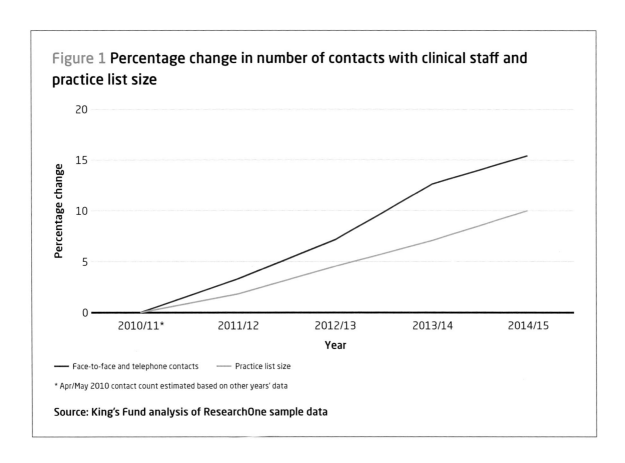

Figure 1 Percentage change in number of contacts with clinical staff and practice list size

— Face-to-face and telephone contacts   — Practice list size

* Apr/May 2010 contact count estimated based on other years' data

Source: King's Fund analysis of ResearchOne sample data

Type of consultations

There were definite changes in how patients interact with their practice. As Figure 2 shows, total face-to-face consultations increased by 13.3 per cent between 2010/11 and 2014/15, while telephone contacts increased hugely by 62.6 per cent over the same period. The proportion of telephone consultations to face-to-face consultations changed from 10 per cent to 14 per cent over the same five-year period.

The average practice responding to our workload survey conducted 979 face-to-face and 288 telephone consultations a week (with an average registered patient list of 10,880). Furthermore, among those practices that provided data on the number of home and care home visits, the average was 13 care home visits and 27 home visits. The proportion of contacts taking place over the phone was around 21.7 per cent, much higher than in the ResearchOne sample.

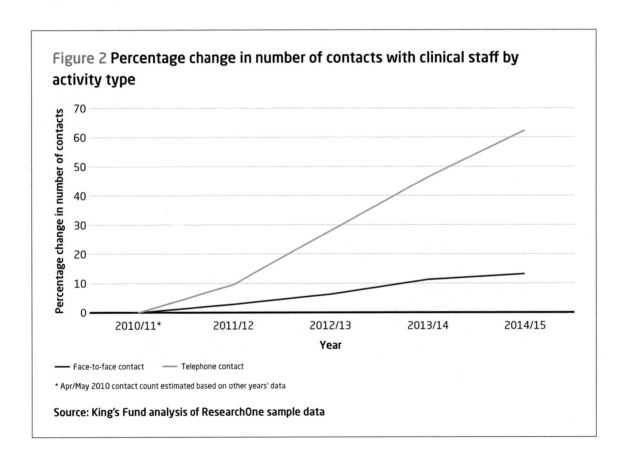

Figure 2 **Percentage change in number of contacts with clinical staff by activity type**

* Apr/May 2010 contact count estimated based on other years' data

Source: King's Fund analysis of ResearchOne sample data

Activity by staff group

The ResearchOne data revealed that total face-to-face and telephone contacts with a GP rose by 15.2 per cent between 2010/11 and 2014/15. The number of face-to-face consultations rose by 12.2 per cent and the average number of face-to-face contacts with a GP per registered patient rose from 3.2 contacts in 2010/11 to 3.67 in 2014/15 (*see* Figure 3). Telephone contacts with patients by GPs increased hugely by 68.5 per cent over the same period.

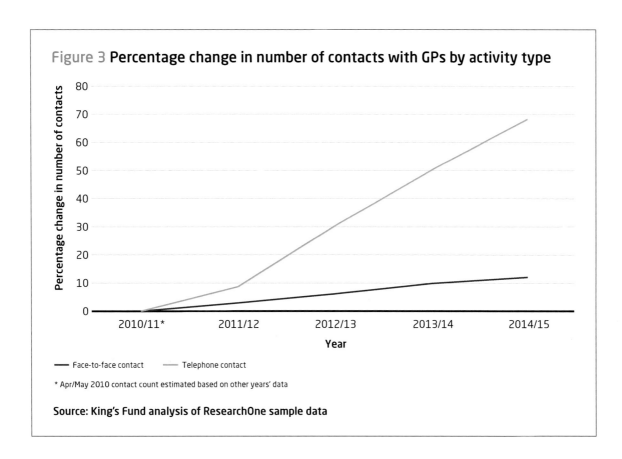

Figure 3 **Percentage change in number of contacts with GPs by activity type**

Face-to-face contact   *Telephone contact*

* Apr/May 2010 contact count estimated based on other years' data

Source: King's Fund analysis of ResearchOne sample data

Total activity performed by nurses in the sample increased by 18.1 per cent (*see* Figure 4). Within this there was a 17.4 per cent increase in face-to-face activity, but a 70 per cent increase in telephone contacts over the same period.

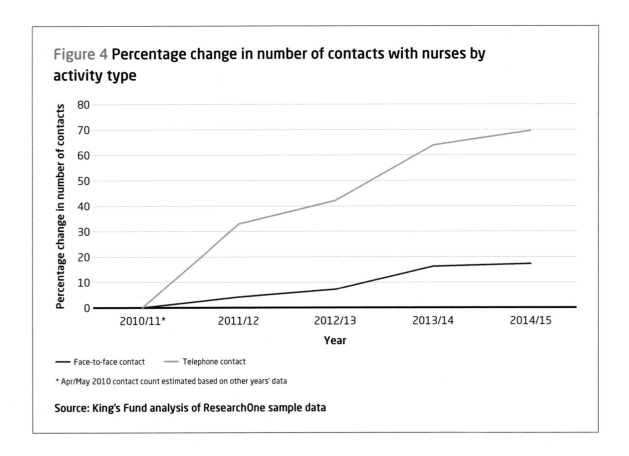

Figure 4 **Percentage change in number of contacts with nurses by activity type**

— Face-to-face contact   — Telephone contact

* Apr/May 2010 contact count estimated based on other years' data

Source: King's Fund analysis of ResearchOne sample data

Activity by age group

While 18–64-year-olds account for over half of clinical staff contacts, their share has been declining (total contacts grew by only 4 per cent). In contrast, the share of clinical staff contacts taken up by patients over 85 increased by 16 per cent, from 3.6 per cent to 4.3 per cent (a 28 per cent increase in total contacts). The share of clinical staff contacts taken up by children and those aged 65–84 has remained stable.

Summary

It is clear from our data analysis that activity in general practice has increased significantly over the past five years. However, our qualitative research found that the feelings of pressure in general practice could not solely be explained by an increase in volume of contacts. In the following sections we examine the changing nature of the general practice workload and consider how patient, system and supply-side factors have further impacted on this.

Patient perceptions of general practice

In light of this rising activity in general practice over the past five years, how has the patient experience changed? Have patients had trouble booking appointments? Are they seeking support from alternative sources like accident and emergency (A&E) or opting for self-care? And has their perception of the quality of the service they are receiving changed?

The national GP patient survey, carried out twice yearly by Ipsos MORI on behalf of NHS England, seeks views from more than 1 million people in the United Kingdom. It asks patients a set of questions about their experience with their GP practice, including questions about accessing GP services, the ease with which they got an appointment and how long they had to wait. The survey suggests that the number of people who are unable to get a GP appointment when they want one has been slowly increasing. In the latest survey, 85 per cent of patients said they were able to get an appointment to see or speak to someone the last time they tried, down from 87 per cent in December 2012. (Changes in the survey question mean some data prior to 2012 is not directly comparable.) People were also more likely to say their experience of making an appointment was 'fairly poor' or 'very poor'; fewer people were happy with the amount of time they had to wait for an appointment and patients are finding it increasingly difficult to get through to practices on the phone (Ipsos MORI 2016).

The latest GP patient survey also shows a slight decline in the ratings patients gave to their interactions with staff in GP practices. Compared with 2012, there was a slight reduction in the proportion of patients saying their GPs and nurses were good at listening (87.1 per cent and 78.3 per cent respectively), giving them enough time (84.9 per cent and 79.3 per cent respectively), treating them with care (82.6 per cent and 77.2 per cent respectively), and explaining and involving them in decisions (74.0 per cent and 65.3 per cent respectively). The survey reveals that overall satisfaction with general practice has declined since 2012, with the proportion of patients describing their experience as 'poor' or 'very poor' increasing to 5.1 per cent from 4.0 per cent. The proportion describing their experience of care as 'good' or 'very good' has fallen from 87.5 per cent to 84.9 per cent, even though this is still a high level of satisfaction (Ipsos MORI 2016).

A different survey presents a similar picture of high but falling satisfaction rates. The British Social Attitudes (BSA) survey asks members of the public (who may or may not have used the NHS recently) about their views and feelings about NHS services alongside a host of other questions about society. Its most recent report (2015) found that the satisfaction rate for GP services was higher than for other NHS services, but the satisfaction rate (69 per cent) was the lowest since the survey started in 1983 (Appleby and Robertson 2016).

A review of local Healthwatch reports by Healthwatch England provides further insight into how the patient experience across the general practice system has changed in the past few years. Issues consistently raised by these reports included: difficulty booking appointments; frustration with appointment systems; lack of choice of GP; short or rushed appointments; poor attitudes of staff, particularly reception staff; insufficient information about out-of-hours services; inadequate information and support for people to self-manage or navigate the health system; poor access for people with disabilities; and a lack of translation services (Healthwatch 2015).

In summary, this national evidence suggests that patients are less satisfied with access to general practice and their experience of using GP services than they were in 2012. But this decline has been small and from already high levels of satisfaction. It does, however, suggest that despite an increase in activity over the past five years patients have increasing problems accessing services.

Causes of pressure: patient factors

As general practice is openly accessible, demand is substantially influenced by patient and public beliefs about what the service should offer. High public expectations and demands were a prominent concern among almost all the staff we interviewed and trainees we surveyed. Expectations appeared to focus on several aspects of care, including access, continuity, treatment, and self-care.

Access and continuity

In our fieldwork, people's desire for both rapid access and continuity of care was often raised as a key source of pressure on general practice, particularly by receptionists and administrators. Ensuring rapid access to general practice has been a policy priority for recent governments. The Labour government introduced a target that by 2004 people should be able to see a primary care professional within 24 hours and a GP within 48 hours. This target was withdrawn by the coalition government in 2010. However, access to general practice became a feature of the 2015 election campaign, with all parties promising to improve it.

Public demand for same-day access to general practice is also well documented through the GP patient survey. The latest survey results showed that 40.4 per cent of patients who contacted their practice for an appointment wanted to see or speak to someone on the same day, with 9.9 per cent wanting to see someone the next day and 23 per cent in a few days. More than 75 per cent wanted to see or speak to a GP rather than another member of staff, with only 6.7 per cent wanting to speak to a GP on the phone (Ipsos MORI 2016).

A focus on rapid access can lead to consequences for patients wanting to book routine appointments for non-urgent problems. If a high proportion of appointments need to be set aside to deal with on-the-day demand, the wait for a routine appointment can become very long; in one practice we visited, the wait was regularly more than four weeks. Several of the staff we spoke to felt that patients are usually willing to wait for a period of time to be seen for a non-urgent problem, usually citing a typical period of up to two weeks. However, they believed that if waits for routine appointments exceed this time, then patients often claim their problem is urgent in order to be seen more quickly. This adds to existing pressure on urgent appointment systems and makes it challenging for practices to address non-urgent problems in a timely manner. As some GPs told us, this can lead to inappropriate use of urgent appointments:

> *If you can't offer somebody an appointment in a fortnight, which is your next routine appointment, you tend to just squeeze them in and you see them, so they ring up and they get seen the same day even if it's something that didn't need to be seen, because there isn't an appointment to give them for several weeks.*

The practices we spoke to had implemented a variety of methods to manage demand, particularly for managing same-day presentation of acute onset illness. These included telephone triage schemes and changing skill-mix by using other members of the primary care team (including nurses, pharmacists and paramedics). Evidence suggests that predicting demand for this type of care is relatively straightforward and that such schemes have the potential to effectively manage minor illness (Longman and Laitner 2013; Shum *et al* 2000). Some GPs felt that the introduction of telephone access, while slightly reducing face-to-face time, had placed additional demands on their time:

> *Whereas five or six years ago I might have been having an 18-patient surgery and then four or five phone calls, now it's a 16-patient surgery with 15, 20, 25 phone calls.*

The large growth of telephone triage and consultations can be seen in our analysis of ResearchOne data and the high proportion found in our workload survey. There is no reliable way of ascertaining the average length of these appointments from the available data, although most practices we spoke to assumed that a telephone appointment would take around half the length of a face-to-face appointment. There was no consistent way in which telephone access had been implemented across the practices we spoke to: some had dedicated sessions for 'telephone clinics'; others slotted this work around their face-to-face clinical work. The National Audit Office analysed data from the 2014 GP patient survey and found significant variation in the proportion of patients unable to get an appointment (a range of 0 to 52 per cent), but this variation was not easily explained by demographics, practice characteristics or supply of staff (National Audit Office 2015). The degree of variation in access across the country that cannot easily be explained by other factors suggests that more could be done to enable practices to streamline appointment processes.

The government has promised that everyone in England will be able to see a GP between 8am and 8pm, seven days a week, by 2020. The practices that completed our workload survey (based on a week in October 2015) were open for an average of 57 hours that week. Public appetite for extended hours and seven-day services remains a source of contention, but staff we interviewed generally felt that patients wanted better access during the working week and were using extended hours services not because they were more convenient but because they were unable to access weekday appointments. As one GP noted:

> I'm on the late evening surgery this evening and you would have thought that the type of patients you see there are the ones that work during the day, but actually I still get the older patients, the retired patients coming in and I think that's probably just when they can get an appointment.

While there was less clarity about access outside usual hours, patients' expectations of rapid access were prominent throughout our work. We heard evidence that this demand was placing significant strain on urgent and emergency appointment systems, with one GP commenting that:

> The biggest difference in the past five years probably is the people who are simply unwilling to wait more than 24 hours to be seen or spoken with.

It is not only the speed of access that people value when using primary care services; many people have a preferred clinician, and continuity of care – in terms of a patient consistently consulting the same clinician and developing an ongoing therapeutic relationship – is a characteristic feature of traditional general practice. In the most recent GP patient survey, half of patients reported having a GP they prefer to see, and of these, 36 per cent 'always or almost always' get to see this GP. This has declined from 38.5 per cent in December 2013 (Ipsos MORI 2016). Studies

have found that most people want rapid access and continuity of care rather than one or the other (Boyle *et al* 2010), which was reflected in the experiences of the staff we spoke to. There was a general feeling among staff that this is an unrealistic expectation, with one GP noting that:

> *Patients want immediacy, but immediacy with the doctor of their choice at the time of their choice. And that's a gold standard… We'd all like that, but there seems to be little understanding among patients that that isn't actually possible.*

Studies of reforms in the early 2000s designed to improve access did find that they had reduced continuity of care (Campbell *et al* 2010). There has been renewed focus on continuity through the recently introduced 'named GP' scheme, which requires allocation of a named and accountable GP to all registered patients, beginning with patients over 75 then extending to all patients by March 2016 (personal GP registration came to an end in 2004 and patients have since been registered with a practice). There is a tension between this focus on continuity and the trend towards part-time and portfolio careers in general practice, which we describe in Section 6.

Self-care for minor ailments

Research suggests that most people prefer to self-manage minor ailments and that this preference has declined over time (Rennie *et al* 2012; Banks 2010; Porteous *et al* 2006). A study examining consultation and prescribing rates for acute respiratory tract infections between 1997 and 2006 found decreasing frequency of consultation and antibiotic prescription for colds and other respiratory tract infections (Gulliford *et al* 2009). However, many of the GPs and other practice staff we interviewed did perceive that people's ability and/or willingness to manage minor or self-limiting illness without consulting a health care professional had changed over time. As one GP partner said:

> *When I started in 1999 people didn't want to bother the doctor… There is a greater expectation of a fix… The expectation that you should be seen today about anything, even if it's for advice, and often for what we perceive to be very self-limiting illness. So it's trying to broker the sheer complexity against the demand for – not wishing to sound demeaning – but for the trivial, the self-limiting illness.*

Various reasons were put forward for this reluctance to self-care. Some GPs felt that the reliance on doctors to assess and manage minor, self-limiting illness was a consequence of the breakdown of informal family support networks:

> *Part of it might be reduced self-care I think. It used to be the case most people learned how to look after themselves, passed on family remedies... There's less of that... When you're ill, the first port of call... It's not your mum or dad, it's the GP.*

> *People tend to take a lot less responsibility over their own health these days, and that's in part as a result of families having fragmented, so you haven't got the parents reassuring their daughter that the grandchild's actually okay, it's fine to have a bit of a fever... Because we haven't got that extended family support any more, I think that that has a knock-on effect on expectations.*

There is also significant debate about whether improving access, particularly through telephone triage, has unintended consequences and can actually increase demand (so-called supply-induced demand). A randomised controlled trial (RCT) found that the introduction of telephone triage was associated with an increase in the number of contacts, although not increased costs (Campbell *et al* 2014). Some have argued that telephone triage results in 'trivial' complaints being managed or patients calling more frequently for reassurance about self-limiting conditions (Rosen 2014). However, there is limited evidence that information schemes to divert patients to other sources of treatment and information can effectively improve patients' management of self-limiting illness (Rosen 2014).

While responsibilities for managing our own health are set out in the NHS Constitution (Department of Health 2012c), each individual's motivation and capability to engage in their health and care needs to be understood and their engagement supported (Foot *et al* 2014; Hibbard and Gilburt 2014). Most of the emphasis on supporting people to gain skills has been primarily focused on people with long-term conditions. There is clearly a role for the NHS to give people more skills and confidence to manage minor illness. When GPs are feeling pressured and overwhelmed, time to educate patients in consultations also tends to be eroded. Even with more patient education, patients still want reassurance and indeed diagnosis.

Evidence does suggest that increased access to health information seems to drive demand rather than divert it. For example, an evaluation of the NHS Choices website found that it did modify demand for health services and that frequent users of the site consulted their GP more often. There were also indications that it may have encouraged hard-to-reach groups to appropriately consult their GP. Both these outcomes increased rather than decreased GP workload (Nelson *et al* 2010). Interviewees also suggested that the ready availability of health information had increased workload, particularly because people were unable to differentiate their own symptoms, as one GP noted:

> *[Patients] are unable to determine what's serious and what's not serious. So they come to you and they present a whole raft of symptoms and they haven't got a clue whether that means anything important… And so we're flooded by loads and loads of things… I don't know why, there can't just be raised expectation, it's a deskilling of people's peers.*

During interviews, we were struck by the disparity between the views of administrative staff (who almost all talked about the tendency for people with minor illness to contact the surgery unnecessarily) and those of GPs (who generally did not feel this was as prominent an issue). This appeared to be a result of triaging practices, which meant that GPs were left to deal only with more complex cases.

As indicated earlier, the ResearchOne data suggests that more and more direct patient activity is being conducted as telephone consultations. The pace of this change is not the same for all age groups though; phone consultations seem to be more popular among younger age groups. Telephone consultations as a share of total activity only increased by 0.6 per cent for patients over 85 between 2010/11 and 2014/15, while for the 18–64 age group, the increase was 1.3 per cent.

We were not able to tell from our data analysis whether patients were consulting more often for minor ailments although, conversely, our analysis of the ResearchOne data suggests that those who receive telephone consultations were likely to have more chronic conditions recorded at the start of the consultation than those receiving face-to-face appointments. Though the average number of chronic conditions of patients who have a telephone consultation has remained largely steady after an initial increase, the average number of chronic conditions of people who attend face-to-face appointments has been increasing.

Treatment expectations

There was a strong consensus among our interviewees and survey respondents that patients' expectations of care have increased over time. Some interviewees reported a widespread expectation among patients that they should be prescribed antibiotics for minor illnesses or should receive diagnostic tests or be referred for specialist care when not clinically indicated. The expectation most frequently commented on was that of rapid resolution to problems.

> *There's definitely a shift towards expecting issues to be dealt with in one meeting as it were. There's little tolerance these days of having three or four visits about the same thing or giving things time to evolve to allow us to, sort of, address how we approach a problem.*
> GP

> *Many expect all their problems to be solved within a single appointment alongside sometimes unrealistic demands regarding referrals/investigations/treatments, etc.*
> GP trainee

> *They expect to see specialists very quickly and to see improvements very quickly, even when, for instance, an average back injury recovery is 8–12 weeks, not the two-to-four patients would prefer.*
> GP trainee

Some GPs felt these expectations reflected wider societal changes, as one GP partner noted:

> *The media and political influence of consumerism, choice, 24/7 access drives up demand or the perception of what people are entitled to or what they should be able to have as part of their NHS – what they pay their taxes for. So that has definitely driven up workload because there is an expectation from the public.*

This was echoed by a GP trainee who suggested that pressure from employers and schools meant that people were anxious to get back to work, driving their demands for both rapid access and rapid treatment:

> *A lack of patience to let time do the healing, sometimes understandable as the world (and work) does not stop and moves so quickly they can't afford being left out.*

Patient complexity

General practice was designed to enable GPs to have short consultations with patients where they would either diagnose and treat common health problems or identify those with more serious problems and refer them to specialist care. People are now living longer, with a consequent rise in the number of those living with chronic disease. This, combined with a policy focus on keeping care as close to home as possible, has meant that the key role of general practice is managing people with chronic and often multiple conditions.

The Department of Health's latest *Long term conditions compendium of information*, compiled using data from the Quality and Outcomes Framework (QOF) and the General Lifestyle Survey, suggests that around 15 million people in England have a long-term condition. The number of people with one long-term condition is projected to be relatively stable over the next 10 years but the number of people with multiple long-term conditions is set to rise to 2.9 million in 2018 from 1.9 million in 2008. We know that the likelihood of having a long-term condition increases with age, and by 2034 the number of people aged 85 and over is projected to be 2.5 times that in 2009, reaching 3.5 million and accounting for 5 per cent of the population (Department of Health 2012b).

In the ResearchOne data, the largest growth in the average number of chronic conditions listed in the patient record at the start of the consultation was seen in people aged 85 and over (*see* Figure 5).

Though there are marginal changes in the average number of chronic conditions per patient in most age groups, those aged 85 and over show a much sharper change, with the average number of chronic conditions increasing by 8 per cent, from 3.03 to 3.27 per patient. Some of this increase may be due to better recording of such conditions, potentially driven by incentive payments. However, the fact of having this condition recorded (for example, for a new diagnosis of dementia) will still lead to extra work for the practice in terms of monitoring and follow-up.

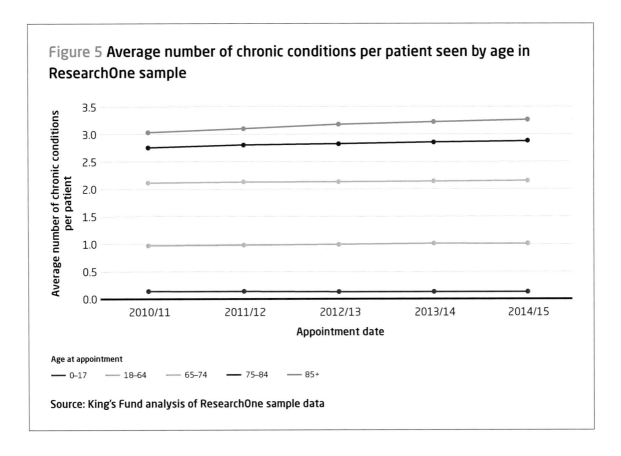

Figure 5 **Average number of chronic conditions per patient seen by age in ResearchOne sample**

Source: King's Fund analysis of ResearchOne sample data

The increasing pressure arising from the prevalence of co-morbidity was a feature of many of our interviews with GPs:

> *These are people who, as we've controlled all their risk factors over the past 10 or 15 years, they've lived longer and gathered more long-term conditions along the way as well... So, diabetes, hypertension, COPD [chronic obstructive pulmonary disease], asthma – all those major disease groups clustering together in the elderly with less support.*

> *Looking at my consultations today, most people had at least two problems to deal with and there's two or three in there who have four or five problems or more.*

Initiatives to improve care for patients with one or more long-term conditions – for example, through the QOF – mean that many actions are needed for each patient, including health promotion, screening, monitoring and other disease management tasks, as well as addressing any other issue the patient might initially present with. This presents a challenge to GPs working to a model of 10-minute consultations:

> *The way the system is set up is, it is set up to enable you to have a 10-minute consultation and within that 10-minute consultation you deal with the reactive stuff. But then you are thinking, 'Oh my gosh, they've got all of those long-term conditions, I'm not really doing anything. I need to...' So you know, you can see that things aren't being addressed but they've not come for that problem.*

At our case study sites, other members of the clinical team were able to support some of this work, with practice nurses in particular taking a role in the management of long-term conditions, as one GP noted:

> *I've also seen a lot of that day-to-day protocol-led management now being devolved to other members of the team, so we now work in a much more multi-skilled way and some of that's very beneficial. So we have some fantastic specialist heart failure nurses, community matrons, etc, who are very able to follow protocols to manage some of these complex patients.*

A study from the University of Bristol found that an average consultation included discussion of 2.5 different problems across a wide range of disease areas in less than 12 minutes, with each additional problem being discussed in just two minutes. Doctors raised problems, in addition to those presented by patients, in 43 per cent of consultations (Salisbury *et al* 2013).

The average length of GP appointments appears to have been increasing in recent years. The most recent national GP workload survey found that average appointment length had increased from 8.4 minutes in 1992/93 to 11.7 minutes in 2007 (Health and Social Care Information Centre 2007). We were not able to accurately ascertain appointment length from our analysis of ResearchOne data. Our survey of 43 practices found an average length of 12.2 minutes (range of 9–15 minutes). In a survey carried out by the Commonwealth Fund in 2015, UK GPs reported the second shortest appointment length (11 minutes) and Germany the shortest (10 minutes) compared to an average of 16.45 minutes across 11 countries. A total of 73 per cent of UK GPs said they were somewhat or very dissatisfied with time spent per patient, the highest dissatisfaction rate across all 11 countries (Osborn and Schneider 2015).

Pharmacy, including polypharmacy and repeat prescribing

The increase in the number of patients with long-term conditions has led to more prescribing, particularly repeat prescribing. Data on primary care prescribing from NHS England between October 2010 and October 2015 shows a 46 per cent increase in antidepressant prescribing, a 93 per cent increase in mucolytics for COPD, a 34 per cent increase in drugs used to treat diabetes, and a 68 per cent increase in anticoagulants and protamine medicines prescribed (openprescribing.net).

The average number of repeat prescriptions generated in a week by practices that completed our survey was 1,091 (those practices having an average registered population of 10,880), ranging from 134 (for a population of 5,714) to 2,606 (for a population of 18,569). Most practices we spoke to have an administrator assigned solely to managing repeat prescriptions every day. GPs reported having up to 70 or 80 repeat prescriptions to authorise in the gap between morning and afternoon clinics. They felt that to fully check a prescription took around three to four minutes, which was clearly not possible in the time available. Despite attempts to streamline processes through electronic prescribing and repeat dispensing, this caused significant pressure on practices, as one administrator noted:

> *Now we've got electronic repeat dispensing, the chemist can't see it. So we're getting a constant barrage of patients saying, the chemist says they've no medications left, because they haven't been downloaded from the NHS computer to the pharmacy. Because it's not the pharmacy, they say go back to your GP, whereas in actual fact, if they wait another day or two, it will then arrive from the NHS computer.*

Diversity and deprivation

Working in communities with high levels of deprivation also puts additional pressure on general practice, which is not necessarily reflected in funding allocations. Evidence shows that patients in the most socio-economically deprived groups experience long-term conditions and multiple morbidity much earlier in life than those in more affluent areas (Barnett *et al* 2012). Areas with higher levels of deprivation also tend to see more patients with mental as well as physical health problems, as reflected in this comment by a GP trainee:

> *I am overwhelmed by patient psychosocial complexity in my deprived area of London.*

A study reported in *The BMJ* in 2014 examined annual consultation rates for 1 million GP-registered people in east London, broken down by national quintiles of the Index of Multiple Deprivation (IMD). The study found that someone aged 50 in the most deprived quintile consults their GP at the same rate as someone aged 70 in the least deprived quintile (Boomla *et al* 2014).

We cannot break down our ResearchOne sample's registered patient populations by IMD rank in the same way; however, we can glean some insights into the use of services according to deprivation rank. Looking at the average number of contacts per registered patient according to IMD rank over the past five years (*see* Figure 6), we found that not only are people living in areas of worst deprivation more likely to access services, they are also using them more frequently.

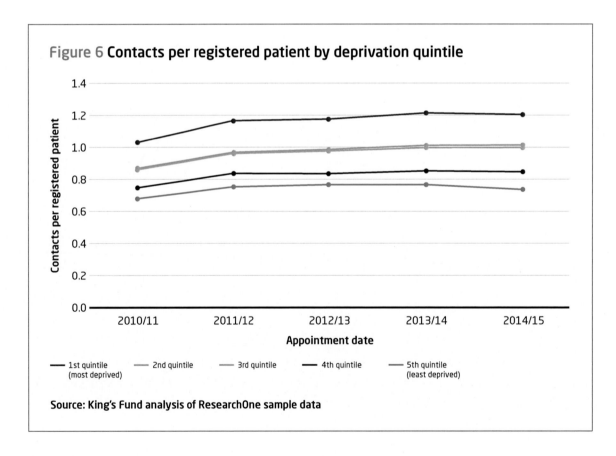

Figure 6 **Contacts per registered patient by deprivation quintile**

Source: King's Fund analysis of ResearchOne sample data

Figure 6 shows a rise in service use in all deprivation quintiles, with an especially sharp increase in the appointments per patient for those in the most deprived quintile, from 1.03 contacts per year in 2010/11 to 1.21 in 2014/15 – a 17.5 per cent increase in contacts per registered patient.

As age typically has a greater effect on chronic conditions than deprivation, we can best see the interaction between deprivation and chronic conditions by narrowing down our age groups. Figure 7 shows the average number of chronic conditions by IMD rank quintile for patients over 65.

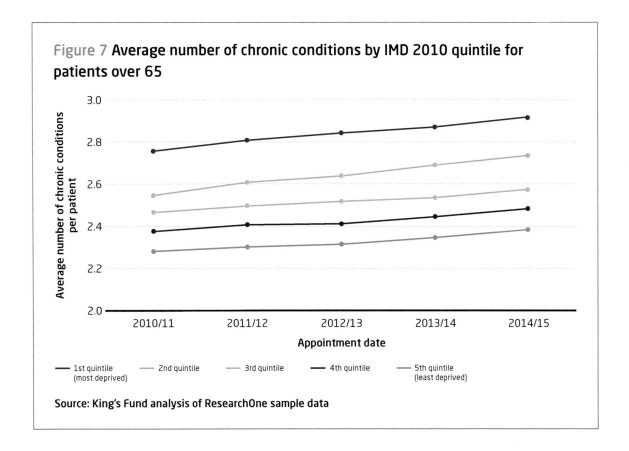

Figure 7 **Average number of chronic conditions by IMD 2010 quintile for patients over 65**

Source: King's Fund analysis of ResearchOne sample data

Patients in all quintiles are showing an increase in the average number of pre-existing chronic conditions they are recorded as having at the time of their appointment between 2010/11 and 2014/15, but as the level of deprivation increases, so does the number of chronic conditions. On top of this, the largest proportional increases in average co-morbidity come in the two most deprived quintiles (a 5 per cent and 7 per cent increase in the most deprived and second most deprived quintiles respectively).

Data on deprivation focuses on relative rank rather than an absolute measure and so we did not find evidence that overall deprivation levels had increased. Rather, we found that the effects of increasing levels of chronic disease were further magnified in deprived areas.

The added pressure of working with diverse populations was raised both in our case study sites and in our survey of GP trainees. There were particular challenges in providing services for practices with high numbers of people from minority ethnic communities who face both language and cultural barriers in accessing care. In one of our study sites, around 30 per cent of the patient population required access to an interpreter. The practice found that using in-house interpreters (trained bi-lingual reception staff) cut down on appointment length but these patients still required at least double the time of other appointments. In addition to difficulty with spoken English, this population had low levels of literacy, in English or sometimes in their native language. GP trainees who responded to our survey also reported the pressures of language issues:

> In London, where I work, patients are often unable to speak good English. Consultations are made difficult and take longer using broken English or through an interpreter.

Most of the information provided for patient education in general practice is printed material, and one of our case study sites suggested it was important to develop innovative ways to communicate with patients who do not have good literacy skills. Supporting patients from communities that do not have English as a first language to navigate the wider health care system has also put additional pressure on practices. Several interviewees reported patients booking appointments to have letters from secondary care explained, or patients missing appointments because they did not understand the letter or got lost travelling to the hospital and so needed re-referral. While it is possible to apply for local enhanced services (LES) funding and other grant-type schemes to support specialist services for such communities, interviewees said this did not address the issue that the core business of general practice was more costly and time-consuming where there are language and cultural barriers to patients accessing care.

⑤ Causes of pressure: system factors

As well as increasing demands and expectations from patients, our qualitative research identified a number of changes within the wider health and social care system that are impacting on the work of general practice.

New services

Medical advances and developments in preventive health care have led to a considerable increase in the number of activities carried out in general practice. GPs and other primary care staff we spoke to showed great enthusiasm for potential improvements to patient care, and largely recognised these as positive changes. However, there was a feeling that this work had not been accompanied by increased resources in terms of staff numbers or funding, as highlighted by these comments from practice nurses:

> *There's just more out there, which is great, but you've got to get it done.*

> *The workload constantly gets bigger and bigger. And we can do that, if we have the funding.*

Immunisations

The past five years alone have seen the addition of numerous vaccines to the immunisation programme, including extending influenza vaccines to young children and pregnant women, shingles vaccines for people in their 70s, and the introduction of rotavirus, meningococcal B and meningococcal ACWY vaccines (Public Health England 2015). All of these are administered in primary care. The GPs and practice nurses we spoke to told us about the implications of this on their workload:

> *Immunisations get increasingly complex and we have more and more immunisations to do. There's no extra provision of time for these. So whereas,*

when I was practising 10, 15 years ago, I might have given two vaccinations for new babies, I'm now giving three or four.
Practice nurse

With the new vaccines that they've brought out, it takes longer to do each one, and to explain to the parents about it… Everything that they add on for us to do just takes more and more time, and any vaccine campaign we have to do, we have to do the mop up… And this is on top of our workload already… It's not rolled out slowly to us first. Quite often you even hear about it in the media before we even get to hear about it. But it's just things that we have to take on board, and we have to add into our already busy workload.
Practice nurse

There have been concerns that the per-vaccination reimbursement GPs receive is too low. To address these concerns, the General Medical Services (GMS) contract agreed for 2016/17 onwards has increased the reimbursement rate by about a quarter for most vaccinations to a flat £9.60 for each vaccine administered in general practice.

New medicines

Increasingly complex medications have been developed and made available for a wide range of conditions. These often require close monitoring of patients, including regular blood tests and other intensive monitoring that adds to the pressures on general practice. Many medications that would once have been under the remit of hospital specialists are now also being managed and monitored in primary care. We discuss this in greater detail later in the report (p 42–55).

In addition to new and complex drugs, the increasing use of medications for primary and secondary prevention – for example, aspirin, statins, antihypertensives and anticoagulants – leads to an increasing number of people requiring these drugs to be prescribed, monitored and reviewed. This has an impact on the processing of prescriptions and also often necessitates additional monitoring such as blood tests, as one GP notes:

Various drugs have come online like statins and, for example, after someone's had a heart attack originally they just came out with a bit of an aspirin and possibly a blood pressure tablet. Now they come out with an aspirin, an ACE inhibitor, a beta-blocker, clopidogrel... You know, the list of medication is huge, a lot of it requiring up-titration, monitoring, regular bloods.

Increasing use of medications inevitably results in an increase in the incidence of unintended side effects and adverse drug reactions (particularly common for statins and a number of antihypertensives), which further drives demand for services.

New preventive services

Preventive work is now a core part of the role of primary care; the Quality and Outcomes Framework (QOF), introduced in 2004, monitors and incentivises practices to undertake large amounts of proactive disease monitoring and prevention. Practices are awarded points for their performance against a long list of targets, and their performance is a significant determinant of practice income. Examples of activity incentivised by the QOF are:

- maintaining and updating disease registers

- regular monitoring of disease control such as recent blood pressure readings for people with hypertension or blood sugar readings for people with diabetes

- annual reviews for a number of chronic conditions including asthma, COPD and diabetes

- recording risk stratification scores for people with risk factors for certain conditions such as the 'CHA2DS2-VASc Score' to assess stroke risk in people with atrial fibrillation

- vaccinating high-risk groups against influenza

- developing and regularly reviewing care plans for people with dementia.

The precise requirements in the QOF are amended annually (NHS Employers 2015). All of the practices we visited commented on the impact of working towards the QOF on their workload:

With QOF and chronic disease management... Right across the board from our nursing team to our admin team to the doctors, we are all dealing with a lot more chronic disease management.
GP partner

There certainly is more routine follow-up type work. Whether it's to do with the QOF or rheumatoid reviews or mental health reviews or dementia reviews or cardiovascular reviews, it feels like there's a lot more planned chronic disease management which can, I think, sometimes make that day seem a bit longer.
GP partner

All of the practices we visited dedicated significant administrative resources to bringing patients back in for follow-up. Some practices had developed systems to anticipate and spread this workload by offering annual reviews throughout the year:

The patient gets a letter when it comes up to their birthday telling them they've got to go and see a health care assistant. They book in to see the health care assistant when they get their bloods, their blood pressure, dementia screening, alcohol screening and other various different bits and pieces. Then they go on to see the nurse if they need a diabetic check or an asthma check. And then they go on to the doctor, who then goes through all their medicines and does a full medicines review and updates them if everything is okay for a full year. Rather than patients rolling up every month with this and that, the idea is to try and do a whole chunk, once a year. So that's sorted and then the patient hopefully will only present with proper emergencies or proper new problems in between times.
GP partner

Some GPs told us that comprehensive reviews and effective preventive work necessitate extended appointment slots, placing pressure on already stretched appointment systems, as one GP partner noted:

The aspiration of trying to deliver gold standard requires a lot of time.

Activity must be correctly coded to receive the appropriate QOF points, which creates a substantial administrative workload for clinical and non-clinical staff:

These are not simple things… You have been doing them but now you've actually got to, you know, you've got the templates for it and you've got to provide that time. You've got to call patients in… You find that you need more admin staff, you need more people on the front desk.

New clinical guidelines

Some GPs and practice nurses we interviewed reported an increase in activity driven by clinical guidance, as did respondents to our survey of GP trainees.

> *More guidelines/protocols and multiple co-morbidities means general practice and clinical medicine in general are increasingly complex and time-consuming, and no additional time has been allowed for this.*
> GP trainee

> *Guidelines; blood pressure's coming down, cholesterol levels are coming down. We've got to push people to targets.*
> GP partner

Comprehensive, evidence-based clinical guidance is published regularly by the National Institute for Health and Care Excellence (NICE). NICE guidance includes recommendations regarding diagnosis, investigation, referral and management of a wide range of conditions. Many guidelines are relevant to the work of GPs, and can create additional activity when followed correctly. For example, diagnosis of hypertension should be made following ambulatory blood pressure monitoring. Where a GP may once have made a diagnosis based on high readings during a single appointment, a referral may now be made for ambulatory monitoring (involving the patient wearing monitoring equipment for an extended period with regular readings taken automatically) with a subsequent follow-up appointment to discuss the results and initiate any necessary treatment (NICE 2011). In June 2015, NICE published guidelines on 'Suspected cancer: recognition and referral', which lowered referral thresholds, requiring GPs to send many more people with non-specific or early signs of possible cancer through cancer referral pathways (NICE 2015). It is also worth noting that this guidance often adds new things to do rather than replacing outdated practice; as our understanding of clinical approaches and technologies to manage long-term conditions develops, so will the work required of GPs.

Public health campaigns

Staff at the practices we visited also told us about the influence of public health campaigns – particularly those focused on cancer – on demand for appointments. These campaigns often prompt people to consult their GP if they have certain signs or symptoms. Since the Be Clear on Cancer campaign was launched by

Public Health England in 2010, a number of regional and national campaigns have promoted early recognition of signs and symptoms of common cancers with the aim of boosting early diagnosis and increasing survival rates. Evaluation of the 2012 national lung cancer campaign showed that GP attendances for a persistent cough in the over-50s increased by 62 per cent during the campaign period when compared with the same period in the previous year, equating to an additional 2.99 visits per practice per week (Cancer Research UK 2014).

Fit notes and non-NHS work

All practices described completing significant volumes of non-clinical work, such as producing reports and certificates. NHS GPs are required to issue, free of charge, statements of fitness for work for people who require time off or amended duties due to conditions affecting their ability to work. The amount of time spent dealing with requests and the internal processes for doing so seemed to vary markedly between practices depending on the patient population.

Statements of fitness for work were introduced in 2010, replacing sick notes. Doctors may recommend that a person is unable to work, but can now also recommend that they may be fit for work with support or adjustments by their employer. A certificate is not required for the first seven calendar days of absence as people can self-certify for this period. However, GPs told us that people are increasingly asking for notes within this period, often at the request of their employer.

While NHS GPs are statutorily obliged to provide statements of fitness for work, they are not obliged to undertake many other non-clinical tasks such as completing insurance reports and letters. However, most practices offer these services, often at a charge. Many of the staff we spoke to, both clinical and administrative, had observed an increase in these requests over recent years.

> *All proof has to come from a GP and the last GP you've seen... It's creating a huge workload for us.*
> GP partner

Examples of the tasks being completed by the GPs we spoke to include: producing medical reports for insurance companies, solicitors and employers; producing reports for gyms to certify that people are 'fit to exercise'; completing forms for the Department for Work and Pensions (DWP) regarding attendance allowance or personal independence payments; and writing letters to schools to confirm that a child is unable to partake in activities such as swimming. Some GPs felt that organisations are diverting responsibility and risk away from themselves by passing it to a GP:

> *There's an increasing volume of work coming from [non-NHS activity] as well. You know, schools want letters for a cold. Airlines want letters for carrying a prescription on a plane. Employers want letters as well as sick notes just to explain a bit more about what's going on. Employers are asking for occupational health reports when we're not occupational health doctors... It's all just increasing levels of paperwork, again because everyone's trying to protect themselves from legal action, to make sure that they've discharged their own duties.*

Despite the fact that practices could charge for this work, when they were under pressure it represented extra (and not strictly necessary) work to be factored in to the working day.

Relationships with the wider system

Interviews at our case study sites revealed prominent concerns about changing relationships with the wider health and social care system. Many interviewees expressed the view that as the health and social care system comes under more and more pressure, it is general practice that has to pick up the pieces:

> *So all the other services can close their doors... And we can't. They just say, 'We haven't got the capacity'. I'm not disputing what they're saying, but why... How come we've got GPs who've got, if you like, elastic capacity, and they haven't?*
> GP

Relationships with some services in particular (as outlined below) were felt to impact significantly on the workload of general practice.

Relationships with community nursing services

All the practices we visited reported that the work of community nurses has changed significantly in recent years, with consequences for general practice. Community nursing teams are responsible for offering nursing care to people in their own homes. They commonly provide phlebotomy, administration of medication (including injections), catheter care, percutaneous endoscopic gastrostomy (PEG) feeding, end-of-life care, wound care and chronic disease management. Community nurses often care for patients with complex health needs and traditionally work closely with primary care.

Recent pressures on community nursing are well documented; there are growing numbers of older people and people living with frailty and multi-morbidity who require nursing care in their own home. This has been accompanied by a drive to offer more care close to home, prevent unnecessary hospital admission and facilitate early discharge. This leads to increasing levels of acuity and complexity being managed in the community (Foot *et al* 2014). Despite the increasing demand for community nursing services, there has been a decline in the number of nurses working in this setting, particularly those with a district nursing qualification (Addicott *et al* 2015).

GPs told us that they once felt close to community nursing teams and regularly relied on them for help with blood testing, ongoing monitoring and preventive interventions associated with the QOF. However, they reported that nurses are now rarely based within general practice and mainly focus on managing people who are acutely ill and totally housebound. This means they are rarely able to do more preventive, chronic disease management tasks, except for patients already on their caseload.

> *The district nursing service is under a lot of pressure... District nurses have to be absolutely strict that those patients have to be housebound... They are under so much pressure.*
> Practice nurse

> *Now they won't go and see our housebound patients, unless they see them for their own reasons. So we've then got to find the resources to go and do that. And that's changed quite a lot. Before, they used to be helpful and used to look after our patients. Now, they don't. So obviously, they look after their dressings when they come out of hospital and so on... But they don't do the full range of treatment we feel is necessary.*
> Practice nurse

The impact of this on the workload of GPs and practice nurses came across strongly in our interviews:

> We tend to find it difficult with housebound patients… It's hard for us to go out to them when the district nurses might not have as much time to go out to them to review their chronic conditions.
> GP

> The diabetics… The housebound ones… We'd pass it to the district nurses, community nurses, to go out and do their bloods and their foot check… The doctor would review their medications… But the district nurses would normally just go out and do their annual reviews. But if they're not on the district nurse caseload, if they're not already dealing with that patient, then this year it's been a case of, well, 'They're not on our caseload, we're not able to deal with them'.
> Administrator

We heard some concerning suggestions that this may change a GP's ability to instigate the most effective medical management due to considerations about the practicalities and feasibility of ongoing monitoring:

> Whereas before I might start medication… Getting someone to go to them and start the medication, have the district nurse check the blood pressure, check if it's okay… Now you can't do that. A doctor has to go out and do it. Or you might not initiate certain therapies because it would be harder to monitor.
> GP

We did hear examples of good communication between community nursing and primary care teams. One practice we visited did still have community nurses based in the same building; staff told us how this affected communication and teamworking:

> I think because they're in this building it helps a lot to know they're just there… When we've got patients who maybe the district nurses haven't turned up, I'll quickly run down here and be like, 'What's going on?'
> Health care assistant

7 8

Getting in touch with district nurses, or specialist nursing teams, I've never really had an issue. If they've been out of office, there's always a mobile that you can leave a message on, and they'll get back to you within the hour, or a couple of hours, or something like that.
GP

Relationships with mental health services

The vast majority (90 per cent) of adults with mental health problems are supported in primary care (Mental Health Taskforce 2016). The mental health sector is facing significant pressures, with key challenges around funding, capacity and demand (Gilburt 2015). Access to mental health services was raised as an issue by interviewees at all of our case study sites. A number of interviewees felt that mental health services have raised eligibility thresholds – often to a greater degree than other service areas – leaving many patients (including those with complex and high-risk needs) to be managed in primary care. Some GPs expressed concern over the level of risk they felt they were carrying in the absence of specialist support.

The community mental health team again is able to say, 'We don't have the capacity'.
GP

The mental health team only really see people who pose a risk… If I have a patient who has got crippling anxiety, really wants to get it sorted, I've tried loads of different tablets and they're not getting on with any of them and they're not suitable for CBT [cognitive behavioural therapy] in the community… I can't refer that patient to secondary care any more… They'll say because the patient's saying, 'Well I don't want to kill myself but it's running my life', they won't see them.
GP

I think mental health services are stretched to breaking point. What we're seeing increasingly is some of the very unwell, complicated patients who were kept on caseload because they were high risk being discharged back saying 'Please refer back if there's a problem'. Next week there's a problem, in they go again, because the mental health provider is under pressure to keep their caseloads down. So mental health services feel like they really are stretched.
GP

Increasing levels of multi-morbidity (evident in our data analysis) may affect demand for mental health support in primary care; a previous analysis by The King's Fund highlighted the frequent association between long-term physical and mental health problems, indicating that 12–18 per cent of NHS expenditure on long-term conditions is linked to poor mental health, most often anxiety and depression (Naylor *et al* 2012). GPs have a key role in managing these conditions (Naylor *et al* 2016).

Access to evidence-based talking therapies in primary care has improved following the introduction of the national Improving Access to Psychological Therapies (IAPT) programme. However, there is considerable variation in availability; provision of psychological therapies for adults with common mental health problems is estimated to be meeting only 15 per cent of current need (Mental Health Taskforce 2016). Interviewees at one of our case study sites reported the benefits of having mental health workers based within their practice; however, access to psychological therapies remained problematic across the other sites.

> *Of course we should be using more talking therapies. I don't think you'd find a GP who would dissent from that point of view, but we've got to be able to access the talking therapies, haven't we?*
> GP partner

Relationships with care homes

The role of GPs in supporting patients in care homes has been a source of recent controversy. A British Geriatrics Society report (Martin *et al* 2011) found that co-ordinated health services for care homes were lacking, with a variety of arrangements in place. Some homes were contracting directly with local GP practices, some were receiving care through local enhanced services (LES) arrangements, and others were relying solely on traditional GP home visits. Practices in two of our case study sites with nursing homes in their catchment reported some pressures resulting from changes in the nursing homes.

> *There's fewer numbers of beds and the thresholds for reaching care home, or residential and nursing home status have raised enormously in the past five years, which means that the intensity and volume have really increased...*

Yesterday I think there were 18 visits and I think nearly half of them, certainly seven or eight, were from one nursing home.
GP

People resident in nursing and care homes now have increasing medical needs. Whereas previously these patients may have been managed in a hospital setting by a consultant team supported by junior doctors, they now tend to be managed by a visiting GP. Practices also reported that they believed care home staff were less confident about managing risk, perhaps due to fears about regulation and litigation.

We live in quite litigious times so they constantly have to cover their own back, don't they? Everything that happens they want to be able to write down that they've spoken to the doctor. And sometimes contacting the GP at a much lower threshold than perhaps a relative would do at home, or the patient would have done themselves if they were still at home.
GP

We were not able to easily determine changes in the numbers of care home visits from the ResearchOne data. Our workload survey suggested that the average practice carried out 13 care home visits in the sample week, though these may have covered more than one patient.

Relationships with social care services and the third sector

In our qualitative fieldwork, we heard little about relationships with local authority social services. Practices that completed our workload survey reported an average of just 2.5 referrals a week to local authority social services, compared to an average of 20 referrals to other non-NHS services and 29 referrals to NHS community services. Interviewees suggested this was mainly because referrals to social care were more likely to be managed by community health services, particularly community matrons.

[Social Services] are a mystery. And trying to get hold of Social Services is a nightmare. When you find that someone needs a social worker, you just hope someone else has to do it. And it normally is finding a telephone number or faxing off a form and hoping for the best. Occasionally, you get through fairly quickly, especially for children in emergencies. But by and large, it can be quite difficult.
GP

One practice had access to an integrated health and social care provider, which had led to some benefits:

> *Integrated working seems great in terms of the quality, and in terms of the ability to get the person the right care at the right time in a sensible, joined-up way... But it looks as if the budget has gone up more than it might have done if people were fighting over who's going to pay for what.*
> GP

We heard many examples of initiatives working with the voluntary sector to access wider care services, including community navigators, patient champions and health coaches.

> *We have community navigators here who are employed through the voluntary sector... It's really about having somebody that supports the wellbeing agenda and helps an individual to access all the opportunities that there are within the voluntary sector.*
> GP

> *One of the things that's a real strength of ours is our third sector involvement, so we've built up really strong links with community services... Whenever there's something going on, we'll try and get a piece of that, so this Practice Champions project... That was a Lottery-funded project, where 40 of our patients were trained up to be Practice Champions. We've got very good links with our health trainers... They run local exercise classes. We asked them to set up a pain support group, so now that's patient-run by the Practice Champions.*
> GP

We did find, though, that these initiatives were often pilots or only temporarily funded:

> *We set up for a while, there's a really good project called An Emotional Wellbeing Project, which was basically a hand-holding service where the workers spoke other languages and we got some extra funding to spread that out... It was analysed by the University and shown to be brilliant... But the funding ran out and they just disappeared... We used to have a Citizens Advice worker that was fantastic, but the funding went for that... And we used to have an occupational worker that*

would help people to start looking at work issues and that kind of thing, so those things we've lost and it's a real shame, because we felt that it really supported our work.
GP

Relationships with services out of hours

Clinicians we spoke to were, in the main, positive about out-of-hours GP services, although many reported issues with accessing other services out of hours:

It's very difficult to access social care and a lot of even medical, like mental health services in the out-of-hours environment... The thing with the out of hours is that actually the majority of the day is out of hours, isn't it, and the vast majority of the week.
GP

One GP recounted an incident of working for the local out-of-hours GP provider and spending more than three hours travelling to change a blocked catheter (a task that took 15 minutes) because there was no alternative nursing service available out of hours.

Relationships with secondary care

The relationship between general practice and secondary care has significantly changed in recent years. There are many reasons for these changes, including: a policy ambition to deliver more care closer to home; changes in commissioning structures and payment mechanisms; developments in medical technologies; and increasing sub-specialisation, to name but a few. These have affected the workload of general practice in a number of ways.

Referral

GPs made more than 13 million referrals to hospitals for elective (planned) care in 2014/15 (Health and Social Care Information Centre 2015c), a number that has been rising since 2010/11, but shows particular growth from 2013/14 (*see* Figure 8). In our workload survey, the typical GP made a referral for secondary or tertiary care in approximately every tenth contact.

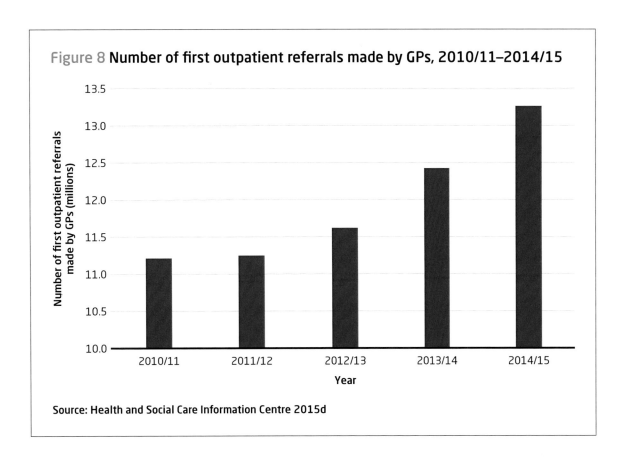

Figure 8 Number of first outpatient referrals made by GPs, 2010/11–2014/15

Source: Health and Social Care Information Centre 2015d

The number of patients referred by their GP to secondary care for a suspected cancer grew 74 per cent between Q4 2009/10 and Q4 2014/15, and the number of those subsequently diagnosed and treated for a cancer rose by 31 per cent (NHS England 2016a). The number of follow-up to first outpatient attendances has remained largely steady over the same period, at approximately 2.3 follow-ups to each first outpatient attendance. Changes in referral processes have resulted from attempts to improve the quality of referrals, manage waiting times and manage demand. As previous work by The King's Fund found, the focus of referral management 'tends to be on managing demand rather than improving quality' (Imison and Naylor 2010).

GPs we interviewed tended to have negative opinions of referral management schemes for a number of reasons. They felt that such schemes had affected their ability to ask for support, guidance and opinion from secondary care colleagues.

> *I think relationships with the hospital are really poor. I think they are far poorer now than they were 10 years ago. I think the days of being able to phone up a*

consultant and ask for some advice seem to be long gone and there are one or two who you can get hold of – email seems to be the preferred way – and often you don't get the advice that you want.
GP

I think what I do miss is, in years gone by, having that phone call with a consultant and saying, 'Do you know what, I'm worried about so and so, is there any way you could fit them into your clinic next week?'
GP

Some GPs felt that the development of standard disease protocols had affected their ability to get flexible support and advice:

So we've got pathways we now have to stick to and follow. And if you sort of deviate from the pathway, the referral just gets bounced back to you. You may have written what you think is a fantastic letter, maybe just asking for a bit of advice, and it just ends up back on your lap… Or they end up getting referred, when actually, what you want is a consultant to have a look at your letter and go, 'Oh, yes, I think we should see them' or 'No, this is what I think we should try in primary care'.

Examples of good practice usually included being able to speak directly and informally to secondary care clinicians either by phone or through visiting the practice and discussing cases more formally.

We did find that administrative staff were more positive about referral management schemes, not least because it gave them a single point of contact for chasing up referrals, rather than trying to navigate the complexities of a hospital system.

They [referral management service] have got access to the hospital system as well, so if a patient phones up and says, 'Oh I was referred 10 weeks ago, I've not heard anything and we can't get through to the hospital', if we phone RAS [referral assessment service] they'll just look for us… Or if we don't know where to send a referral, rather than trying to get through to the hospital to find out, if we just phone RAS then they just help us straight away.

Most clinical commissioning groups (CCGs) seek to prevent referrals within secondary care (consultant-to-consultant referrals), partly because the volumes have risen and partly to ensure that patients always have a choice of where they want to be treated. Previous research by The King's Fund found some anecdotal evidence to suggest that the introduction of Payment by Results has driven hospitals to record a lot of their (previously unrecorded) internal consultation activity, and so approval by GPs would be expected to curtail growth in consultant-to-consultant referrals (Imison and Naylor 2010). However, our work generally found that this resulted in more work for GPs and unnecessary extra waits for patients.

> *... the intention was to put choice in patient hands, but actually those patients turn round and say, 'Well, I don't know who the consultants are and who do you think I should see?' So actually I think that that change wasn't really, I don't think, of great benefit for patients, and certainly it's disempowered us.*
> GP partner

The increasing sub-specialisation in secondary care had also led to more complex referral routes which, combined with a drive to reduce consultant-to-consultant referrals in secondary care, had added to the workload of general practice:

> *Everything's become really compartmentalised so you refer somebody in with dizzy spells and collapse and you're not always sure from that initial presentation whether it's neurology or cardiology or ENT but you try your best to get the information to make the decision and they're seen, discharged but back to the GP... When I was a junior doctor, there would be a conversation between the ENT consultant and a neurologist, without having to zigzag backwards and forwards.*
> GP

Some interviewees complained about the practice of secondary care services discharging patients after they had failed to attend an appointment necessitating a re-referral from primary care. One site in particular reported issues with patients who either had literacy problems (they could not read correspondence from the hospital) or issues with complex public transport and were subsequently late for (or missed) their appointments, and so were discharged back to the GP. This issue was raised by the NHS Alliance study and is being addressed by NHS England (Clay and Stern 2015).

Transfer of work from secondary to primary care

The transfer of work from secondary to primary care was a constant theme in our site visits. Much of this was felt by GPs to be entirely appropriate and they expressed a strong desire to offer care closer to home where they had the skills, and indeed capacity, to do this.

> *There's a huge shift out of hospital into general practice. And actually I genuinely support that because I think the hospitals often make people ill because of over-investigation and over-treatment and I'm very much happier to be dealing with it here. But you need to have the resources to do it and our resources have gone down not up over the past decade and yet despite that, we're doing very much more of the things that used to be dealt with [in hospital].*
> GP

However, despite the development of shared care protocols for many services, GPs still reported issues with the inappropriate transfer of tasks from secondary to primary care, including prescriptions from outpatient appointments:

> *… they'd written and asked us to prescribe some testosterone gel but actually they got the dosage wrong on it and what they've written on it doesn't match up with what's in the BNF [British National Formulary]. So we're going to have to go back to them and ask them what they wanted to prescribe, but really, if they just prescribed it in the hospital, then the hospital pharmacist would have picked it up and the patient would have had it.*
> GP

> *We have started recently to try and keep a log of occasions where patients come to us with their outpatient prescription. They are often told by pharmacy not to wait, that the wait is long and so they come to us… Where it's a bespoke, dermatological sort of preparation, for example, which costs a lot of money for the community to make up, hundreds of pounds per tub… We don't think it's acceptable.*
> GP

Many programmes designed to increase productivity in secondary care and move care closer to home for patients have transferred activity previously undertaken in secondary care to primary care.

They'll order tests and expect us to follow them up or they will tell us to do pretty much what they would normally do in their follow-up clinics. So, 'Can you every six months reassess this patient for this and do bloods?' And that's traditionally what their follow-up would have been for that department. So they're expecting us to do their follow-up clinic.
GP

Another issue raised was the issuing of sick notes, as some hospitals had reportedly stopped producing them, instead telling patients to phone their GP:

That's obviously creating more work for us, because before, if they're in hospital for a week, the consultant just used to give them the sick note to cover them during their hospital stay. But now they say 'Contact your GP and they'll do the sick note'. But sometimes, if we've not had the discharge summary, that's more work for us because we've got to phone the hospital to find out why they are in hospital.
Administrator

Communication

Managing communication from secondary care was perceived to take a significant amount of time in general practice, both for administrative and medical staff. Document management from secondary care was a particular issue; while the tasks were often appropriate to primary care, this resulted in much longer times to process correspondence to ensure that no tasks were missed (and they might be buried in the body of a letter). This sometimes represented an inappropriate transfer of risk, as two GPs commented:

Historically, you'd have a pile of mail where it was for information and you'd just sort of skim read it and there'd be nothing very much to be done. You'd realise there'd been an element of specialist attention that had applied scrutiny to that individual, but actually there were minor changes. Now, every letter has an action point in it, so there'll be a blood test that'll require monitoring.

Even just processing mail from hospitals takes, I would say, 50 per cent more time than it did even five years ago, because so much is being demanded of us by secondary care teams that wasn't previously... Not just handing back patients but asking us to do tests, asking us to forward information, asking us to refer on rather than them doing referrals themselves, which happens, as we know, for a variety of reasons, usually funding.

GPs also reported extra contacts with patients as a result of patients experiencing issues with administrative processes within secondary care:

> *Yesterday… I had 25 maybe 30 phone calls at the end of morning surgery… A lot of it is due to hospitals cancelling operations or people chasing outpatients or histology results.*

> *I think we're seeing far too many people who we're seeing just because the system isn't working. The hospital appointment system isn't working, operations are being cancelled, they're chasing results, I think.*

We did hear examples of good communication, particularly the role of electronic communication:

> *[Hospitals] sending out an instant, on-the-day discharge letter, computerised letter, which we can see, which is immediately attached to the patient's notes, that's really, really good. Not that long ago we might not get a discharge letter about a patient for three months or something. Somebody had to dictate it, it's being done there and then. You see why they went in, what interventions were made, what treatment, what their medications are, what the plan is, it's very good.*
> GP

However, where hospitals were sending both paper and electronic copies, this was doubling the work of practices, who needed to scan the letters and check that they were indeed duplicates, with no actions outstanding.

⑥ Causes of pressure: supply-side issues

In this section we examine some of the supply-side issues that are adding to the pressures felt by general practice.

Funding

Spending on general practice in England was £9 billion in 2014/15 – a 1.3 per cent growth on the previous year but an overall decrease of 0.4 per cent over the five-year period of our study, as shown in Figure 9 (Department of Health 2015; Health and Social Care Information Centre 2015e).

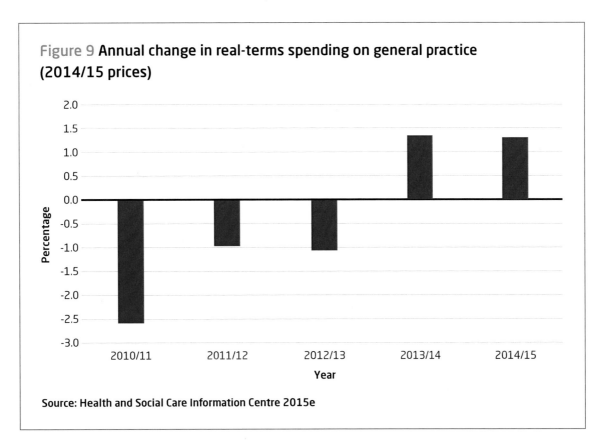

Figure 9 **Annual change in real-terms spending on general practice (2014/15 prices)**

Source: Health and Social Care Information Centre 2015e

Since the large injection of funding into general practice in 2004/5 and 2005/6, which coincided with the introduction of the new GP contract, the share of NHS spending allocated to general practice fell every year to 2014/15. In 2014/15 the share (7.94 per cent) was the lowest in 10 years. The trajectory of GP funding over the years our study covers is shown in Figure 10.

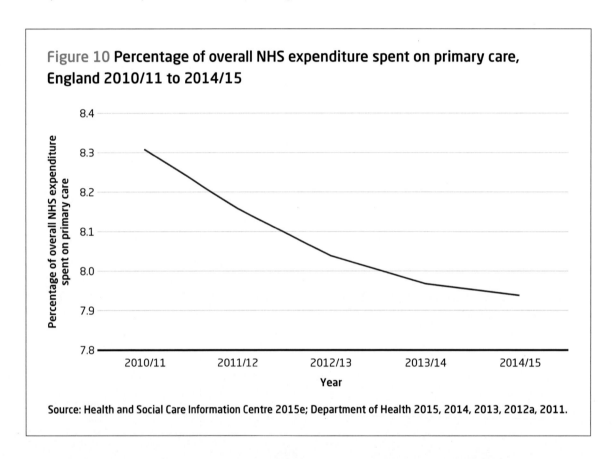

Figure 10 **Percentage of overall NHS expenditure spent on primary care, England 2010/11 to 2014/15**

Source: Health and Social Care Information Centre 2015e; Department of Health 2015, 2014, 2013, 2012a, 2011.

GP funding is complex and covers a wide range of components. While funding for some components (such as premises) has risen, funding for others (such as recruitment and retention and out-of-hours services) has fallen. Cumulatively, there has been an average real-terms decrease of 0.39 per cent over the five years of our study period.

Practices receive funding via three types of contract between general practices and NHS England, covering General Medical Services (GMS), Personal Medical Services (PMS) and Alternative Provider Medical Services (APMS). In October 2015 the government announced that the NHS would offer larger practices and federations with patient lists of over 30,000 people a fourth kind of contract from April 2017.

The details have not yet been agreed, but the government promised that practices would receive funding without it being contingent on meeting Quality and Outcomes Framework (QOF) targets. Practices would be required to provide seven-day access and become providers of services beyond the core set of GP services to encourage integrated care.

Key changes affecting various elements of funding for general practice came into force between 2013/14 and 2014/15. The first was a reduction in the rewards offered for GPs meeting QOF targets, which meant that practices received nearly £400 million less through this route. Some of this reduction was used to fund a new directed enhanced service (DES) related to the proactive management of people assessed as being at risk of an unplanned admission (NHS Employers 2014). The remainder was reallocated to the 'global sum', a payment provided to all GMS practices according to a formula designed to take into account their population's needs. The recently agreed contract for GMS practices for 2016/17 promises £220 million extra funding for a 1 per cent pay uplift through the global sum, an increase in the value of QOF points and an increase in vaccination and reimbursement.

Practices using PMS contracts receive more funding than those on GMS contracts, which is intended to reflect the specific challenges of meeting local needs – for example, where practices are managing particularly challenging populations such as communities without English as a first language, very deprived communities or transient communities. The basic costs of providing core services for such communities are higher. An ongoing review of PMS contracts by NHS England, which is designed to ensure that extra funding received is linked to quality of care, has led to uncertainty and loss of income for some practices (Bounds and Neville 2015).

The Prime Minister's GP Access Fund (formerly known as the Prime Minister's Challenge Fund) was launched as a £50 million fund in 2013 with the aim of improving access to general practice and stimulating innovative ways of providing primary care services. A further £100 million of funding was announced in 2014 (NHS England 2015) for 37 pilot schemes covering more than 1,400 practices, often focused on providing extended opening hours for general practice in the evenings and at weekends. In addition, a £1 billion Primary Care Transformation (formerly infrastructure) Fund was announced in December 2014 to enable general practice to make investment in premises or technology to improve access. Further funding was announced as we went to press, but the details are not yet clear.

Workforce

Doctors

The numbers of full-time equivalent (FTE) GPs (including registrars and retainers, as we have included such staff in our analysis of activity) rose by 4.75 per cent (1,677) between 2010 and 2014 from 35,243 to 36,920. Excluding registrars and retainers the growth was 4.9 per cent. This compares to the number of FTE consultants in other medical specialties grew by 13 per cent over the same period (Health and Social Care Information Centre 2015a).

While the number of FTE GPs increased at a faster rate than the growth in the general population, which rose by around 3 per cent, the number of people aged 85 and over increased from 1.17 million to 1.28 million during the same period (a rise of 19 per cent). This means the ratio of FTE GPs to the number of people in the general population aged over 85 has fallen steadily (*see* Figure 11).

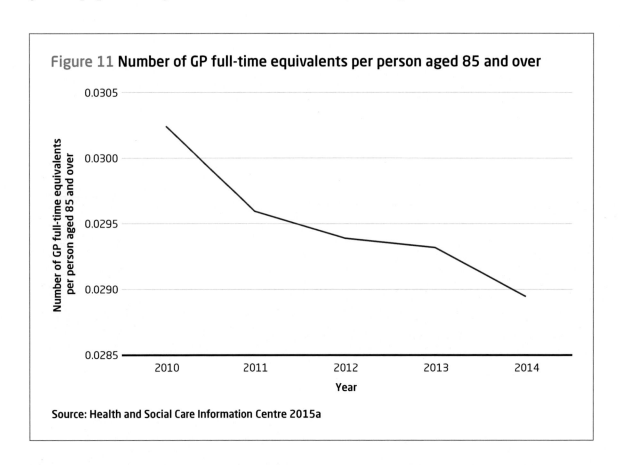

Figure 11 **Number of GP full-time equivalents per person aged 85 and over**

Source: Health and Social Care Information Centre 2015a

As well as seeing their overall funding and their share of the NHS budget fall since 2006, GPs have seen a fall in their personal income during that time. Figure 12 shows how GPs' gross income has changed between 2002/3 and 2013/14, the most recent year for which data is available. As gross income has fallen, GPs have also faced rising expenses. The result is that in real terms, income for GPs fell to the lowest level since 2002/3 (Health and Social Care Information Centre 2015b).

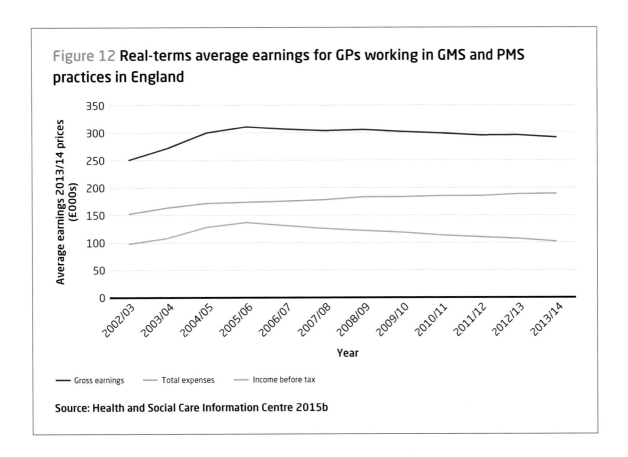

Figure 12 **Real-terms average earnings for GPs working in GMS and PMS practices in England**

Source: Health and Social Care Information Centre 2015b

There is currently a shortage of GPs, which is predicted to worsen. Health Education England, NHS England, the Royal College of General Practitioners (RCGP) and the British Medical Association (BMA) have agreed a '10-point plan' to address this shortage. The government has committed to providing an additional 5,000 GPs by 2020 through a combination of: enhanced recruitment to GP training; improving routes back to general practice for doctors returning to the profession from overseas or from a career break; and measures to retain experienced GPs who are approaching retirement and wish to work part-time or more flexibly (NHS England *et al* 2015).

While this pledge has been welcomed, it is questionable whether it can be achieved given current issues with both recruitment and retention of GPs. There are substantial difficulties with recruitment, both of qualified GPs and GP trainees. In 2014/15, 12 per cent of GP training posts went unfilled despite an additional third round of recruitment intended to boost numbers. The proportion of unfilled places for the 2015/16 recruitment round stood at 17 per cent after the usual two rounds, prompting a third round for the second year running (Rimmer 2015). Vacancy rates vary significantly and recruitment problems are greatest in some of the most deprived areas of the country.

Retention of GPs is also problematic. Between 2005 and 2014 the proportion of GPs aged 55–64 leaving the profession approximately doubled; in 2014, 15.5 per cent of GPs aged 55–59 and 17.9 per cent of GPs aged 60–64 left the profession. Younger GPs are also leaving in growing numbers; the proportion of GPs aged 35–44 leaving the profession increased from 3.8 per cent in 2005 to 6.1 per cent in 2014 (National Audit Office 2015). Between 2009 and 2014, 45.5 per cent of GPs leaving general practice were younger than 50, while 30.6 per cent were aged 50–59, and less than a quarter were aged 60 or over (Health and Social Care Information Centre 2015a). Surveys show that the proportion of GPs expecting to leave direct patient care in the next five years increased from 8.9 per cent in 2012 to 13.1 per cent in 2015 (among GPs under 50) and from 54.1 per cent in 2012 to 60.9 per cent in 2015 (among GPs aged 50 and over) (Gibson *et al* 2015).

One of the findings of our case study research was that very few GPs at those sites were working full-time in patient-facing general practice; this was true of male and female GPs across all age groups. Many were working full-time but had taken on other responsibilities. These included: roles in clinical commissioning groups (CCGs); management tasks in their own practice or in a wider federation; other clinical work such as minor surgery, pain clinics or out-of-hours services; and roles in medical education and academia. Combining activities with clinical work in this manner is commonly referred to as a portfolio career.

We surveyed GPs in training to better understand their intentions for future practice. We asked respondents to state their working intentions for one year, five years and 10 years after qualification. Of the 318 trainees who responded, 31 per cent intended to do full-time clinical work one year after qualification, falling to 11 per cent five years after qualification and just 10 per cent 10 years after qualification. Part-time work appears to be a more attractive option at earlier career stages (preferred by 46 per cent of respondents at one year after qualification, 37 per cent at five years after qualification and 24 per cent at 10 years after qualification).

Portfolio careers become an increasingly popular option at later career stages; the proportion of trainees intending to have a portfolio career increased from 18 per cent one year after qualification to 44 per cent five years after qualification and 49 per cent 10 years after qualification. When asked what types of work they intend to do outside of general practice, the most commonly cited activities were medical education and other clinical NHS work (for example, working in hospitals or urgent care centres). These were each selected by just under a quarter of respondents.

When asked how many clinical sessions (half-day clinics) they intend to work, the majority of trainees favour five to six sessions. The proportion intending to work more sessions than this at one year, five years and 10 years after qualification falls over the respective time periods. These results suggest that the current trend away from full-time clinical working is set to continue and will probably intensify.

The growth of part-time working in general practice has been widely attributed to feminisation of the workforce. However, our survey showed that intentions for part-time or portfolio working are common across both sexes. Although a greater proportion of female than male respondents intend to work part-time and fewer intend to work full-time, these differences diminish over progressive career points. Looking ahead to 10 years after qualification, the proportion of male and female respondents intending to work full-time was 13 per cent and 8 per cent respectively while the proportion intending to work part-time was 20 per cent and 26 per cent respectively. By contrast, a greater proportion of male respondents than female respondents reported that they would choose a portfolio career although again these differences diminish over time. 25 per cent of male respondents and 14 per cent of females respondents plan to have a portfolio career 1 year after qualifying, rising to 51 per cent of male respondents and 48 per cent of female respondents 10 years after qualification. The most commonly cited reason for not pursuing full time clinical work was 'intensity of the working day' rather than 'family commitments'. These findings suggest that the factors driving changes in working patterns are more complex than the assumed increase in numbers of female GPs reducing their hours to manage family commitments. We discuss the reasons cited by trainees for not wanting to pursue full-time clinical careers later in this report.

There has also been an increasing trend for GPs to work in salaried and locum roles rather than taking on partnerships. This was raised by many GPs we interviewed, and we spoke to a number of GPs who had even given up partnerships in favour of locum or salaried roles.

It was striking in the responses to our trainee survey that partnership is no longer an attractive option for many; 48 per cent of respondents report an intention to be a salaried GP one year after qualifying, 44 per cent intend to be a locum and just 3 per cent intend to be a partner. Five years after qualifying, the figures are 48 per cent intending to be a salaried GP, 13 per cent a locum and 25 per cent a partner. Ten years after qualifying, the proportions intending to be salaried or locum GPs fall to 23 per cent and 8 per cent respectively. Less than half of respondents (45 per cent) intend to be a partner at this stage of their career – a proportion that would traditionally have been much higher.

Trainees report a number of reasons for partnership becoming less attractive:

> *I always liked the idea of a partnership, but this has become much less attractive with time; the increased pressures, reduced work–life balance, reduced income, extra responsibility with reducing benefit.*

> *Lots of uncertainty going forwards, which makes GP partnerships daunting.*

> *At present, with the changes in the NHS and the funding crisis in general practice, I would be wary of the financial commitment of becoming a partner.*

> *Revenue has been gradually declining for GP partners over the past five years at least, making it less attractive to become a partner due to the additional workload it brings. It pays more to be a salaried GP and put in additional locum hours to earn the extra money.*

> *Ideally, I would like to be a partner in a few years but I don't think it's possible in the current climate.*

The wider practice team

The general practice workforce is much broader than just general practitioners. At our case study sites we spoke to a wide range of other staff, including practice nurses, health care assistants, community matrons, pharmacists, other allied health professions, reception and administrative staff and managers.

Nurses

The general practice census in 2014 found that there were 15,062 FTE nurses working in general practice, an increase of 119 (0.8 per cent) on the previous year (Health and Social Care Information Centre 2015a). Practice nurses and health care assistants we spoke to undertook a wide range of roles, including health promotion clinics, health checks, immunisations, phlebotomy, patient education and wound care. Others had developed specialist roles in chronic disease management, cervical screening or minor illness clinics. We also found that as community nursing became more remote from general practice, practices were sometimes opting to use their own practice nurses or health care assistants to carry out home visits, particularly for monitoring.

A systematic review (Laurant *et al* 2005) found that while nurses were sometimes able to substitute for general practitioners, they were not necessarily a cheaper alternative as they tended to have longer consultations and recall patients more frequently. Some GPs we spoke to emphasised the benefits that highly experienced practice nurses could bring but reiterated the view that less highly trained and experienced nurses tended to recall patients or refer on unnecessarily.

There is no surfeit of experienced practice nurses available to general practice, and nursing faces similar issues around recruitment and retention. A survey of general practice nurses in 2015 found that a third are due to retire by 2020 and more than 40 per cent reported that their nursing team did not have sufficient numbers of appropriately trained and qualified staff to meet patients' needs (Bradby and McCallum 2015). The *Future of primary care* report from the Primary Care Workforce Commission, while recognising that there has been an international drive to increase the primary care nursing workforce, highlights a 'general lack of opportunity for nurses to develop their skills, and the poorly defined career paths in primary care nursing. This includes a general lack of governance, especially in general practice, to ensure that all those in the workforce (from healthcare assistants to nurse practitioners) both have and maintain the skills that are required for their roles' (Primary Care Workforce Commission 2015, p 18).

Allied health professions (AHPs) and support staff

There are many other professionals working within general practice – for example, pharmacists, physiotherapists and paramedics. During our research, we heard about a rapid access team staffed by a paramedic and pharmacist who were able to triage and treat minor illness; primary care mental health workers and physiotherapists were also mentioned but they were not usually directly employed by the practice. In our survey, the average practice contracted 0.2 FTE allied health professionals, though on the week we surveyed, they worked 0.3 FTEs on average. The latest GP workforce statistics show that in 2014 there were 16,800 staff working in direct patient care roles in general practice in addition to doctors and nurses, up 2.8 per cent on the previous year (Health and Social Care Information Centre 2015a).

Many practices employ health care assistants to carry out basic assessments, tests, disease monitoring and administration. The relatively new role of physician associate (previously physician assistant) can offer some support in general clinical work, such as seeing people with acute illness.

Practice management

Our overwhelming impression of practice management in the case study sites we visited was one of complexity. Practice managers and administrative staff carry out a wide range of tasks, including finance, staffing, health and safety, reception, IT, document management, repeat prescriptions and referral management. We also observed that practice managers were quite isolated professionally and lacked the support that had often been present in primary care trusts (PCTs). We spoke to a number of CCGs in the course of our research and they reported that there was significantly less access to practical support to implement changes in the practice – for example, new telephone triage systems or other initiatives. A survey of CCGs carried out by The King's Fund and Nuffield Trust in 2015 found that 59 per cent of respondents felt CCGs should offer practical help to practices, but only 27 per cent felt that they did (Holder *et al* 2016).

> *A lot of progress in what we want to do is hampered by lack of support from CCGs because of the risk, lack of support around governance – around legal governance,*

around patient confidentiality governance and record governance, yeah – and just that lack of access to, sort of, managerial expertise that would help us with those decisions and with those conversations.
GP

Practice managers nationally are also reporting pressures. A survey of 471 practice managers reported by *Pulse* magazine found that 44 per cent had already considered applying for a new job, 65 per cent of whom said they would be seeking a new career. Over two-thirds (68 per cent) of all the practice managers surveyed said they were feeling demotivated in their job. 'Workload', 'too much change' and 'a lack of support' were all mentioned as reasons (Lind and Mooney 2013).

We did observe that at the study sites with the most stable workforce, the practice management and administrative teams were very well organised, working together to support the practice in a wide variety of ways. Where this was happening, combined with strong relationships between practice manager and GPs, we observed that it affected how clinicians perceived the manageability of their workload.

Commissioning

As already mentioned, the funding arrangements for general practice are labyrinthine and practice managers face the challenge of seeking out many small sources of funding, each with their own reporting requirements. The practice managers we interviewed and the commissioners we tested our findings with reported that the complexity had increased since the reforms brought in by the Health and Social Care Act 2012.

When... Lansley decided to reorganise the health service, he broke it up, as you know, into lots of different parts and then those different parts commissioned services from general practice, so there are loads of locally enhanced services, commissioned by public health, by NHS England, by the council, by the CCG. And each one has got its own payment method, data collection method, different spreadsheets that you've got to submit on, different queries. MyQuest is an interrogation tool that you have got to run in order to get that cohort of patients all full in order to claim, it's a complete nightmare. Then you have got no easy way of checking whether you have actually been paid for this work because the payment centres are all in different places and you don't have phone numbers for most of them and so you submit an email… And then there is no reply and then you give it a couple of weeks and you submit another email but there is never a phone number to call.

Practice manager

So to be faffing about and claiming this and that, here, there and everywhere, it's so disjointed, it just doesn't seem joined-up thinking at all. You're getting a little funding stream from here and a little one from here and if you don't claim this month you won't get that. What is that about? It's so inefficient that someone is spending full-time doing claims.

Practice nurse

This issue was clearly identified in the 2015 report *Making time in general practice*, published by the NHS Alliance and Primary Care Foundation, which also found that getting paid has become a much bigger burden since the 2012 reforms (Clay and Stern 2015).

It was also reported to us that a great deal of expertise in the commissioning of general practice had been lost at the time of the reforms, with headcount at both NHS England and CCGs much smaller than in PCTs and strategic health authorities (SHAs). It was suggested that this had resulted in an over-defensive approach to commissioning, requiring detailed accounting for each pound spent in primary care and a defensive approach to contracting. Commissioners we spoke to also felt some frustration that a policy and political focus on access had resulted in an adversarial approach to the GP contract (on both sides), which meant that true transformation was hard to achieve.

From 2015/16, NHS England offered CCGs the opportunity to take on delegated powers for contract design and management in general practice. CCGs taking full delegation will have the power to review or renew existing GP contracts, and design new PMS and APMS contracts. They will also be able to design and implement local incentive schemes, which can serve as alternatives to the QOF, LES and DES payment schemes. It is too early to tell what impact these changes will have. A survey of GPs and practice managers in six CCGs conducted in early 2016 found that 83 per cent had not noticed any changes as a result of co-commissioning (Holder *et al* 2016).

Successful implementation of delegated commissioning will require commissioners to have access to comprehensive and real-time data to provide insight into the needs of the population, guide commissioning decisions and assess the subsequent impact on patients.

Regulation

The Care Quality Commission (CQC) introduced a new inspection regime for general practice in October 2014 that has generated controversy, with both the BMA and RCGP calling for an overhaul due to the burden on general practice. We expected to hear more than we did about CQC inspection in our case study visits, but only one of our sites had recently had an inspection. This site was well managed and felt able to deal with the demands of the inspection.

Discussion: the impact of pressure

Much of the narrative about the current crisis in general practice has focused on the increasing volume of consultations as a key source of pressure. Our research also found a significant increase in direct contact with patients (face-to-face and via telephone). Added to this, an increase in complexity and intensity of work, caused by a combination of patient and system demands and supply-side factors, has led to the feeling of crisis in general practice.

Practices have developed numerous ways to help manage the increase in demand for appointments either through triage systems (often telephone-based) or providing services led by other members of the primary care team such as nurses, pharmacists and paramedics. There has been a particular increase in telephone contacts, as evidenced in our data analysis.

The benefits of telephone triage and other such systems used to manage demand in general practice are contested. There are a variety of models that fall under this label, ranging from GPs reserving some of the day's sessions for telephone consultations, through to triage systems where GPs are the first point of contact for patients calling the practice, and they do triage. Other practices use administrative staff to guide patients through a set of questions to determine whether they can offer them an appointment with another professional in the team (eg, a nurse or pharmacist). A trial of telephone triage carried out in 2014 found evidence that giving patients seeking on-the-day appointments a telephone consultation with any GP or nurse in the practice increased contact rates (Campbell *et al* 2014). Alternative models like same-day triage by the patient's usual GP (where possible) were not tested in this trial, but proponents of systems like Doctor First and GP Access argue that guaranteeing same-day access to a GP for triage is only one part of the intervention that helps practices manage demand. It comes alongside an effort to look at and change a practice's whole systems and processes, drawing on quality improvement methods.

Whatever the benefits in managing increased numbers of contacts, increased numbers of telephone consultations increases the number of clinical decisions to be made in a short space of time (often based on relatively little information). It may also generate other actions such as following up with secondary care, generating prescriptions or requesting investigations. On top of this, practice staff still need to manage their face-to-face clinical work, which is itself becoming more complex.

Our analysis found that GPs are increasingly seeing patients with multiple long-term conditions, which requires them to manage complex processes and make difficult decisions in a short time with little respite, resulting in a very intense working day. In fact, schemes to manage minor illness using telephone triage or other members of the primary care team were, in some ways, exacerbating this feeling of intensity in face-to-face work, as expressed in these comments from GPs:

> *You rarely see anybody who's just got one problem. You don't see really any just basic chest infections, exacerbation of asthma, sore throats. The nurses see all those things.*

> *Partly it's because we have been trying to be clever about the way that we manage patients so we have instituted nurse-led clinics, we're using telephone appointments, we're trying to make sure that the least qualified person who will fulfil the role does the job, and that's great. Except you no longer have the breaks any more.*

> *We have tried to be quite clever in utilising the skills of the nursing team to take on extra roles but what that has done is, it's meant that you don't have the simple things any more and everything is complex.*

Each patient consultation also generates significant administrative work that may have to be done outside of the scheduled appointment time. This includes: basic data entry and record-keeping; entering data for QOF and other schemes; and referrals to community and secondary care, and the subsequent document management related to those referrals. Complex cases also generate a huge volume of tests – for example, blood tests, imaging, cardiac monitoring and neurophysiology results – that GPs must then check, process, code and safely action on a daily basis. Issues of communication with secondary care in particular, highlighted both by our research and other studies (Clay and Stern 2015), have exacerbated workload pressures and are a major cause of workload stress, commonly cited by GPs as a reason for leaving the profession early (Primary Care Workforce Commission 2015).

Demand for rapid access also makes continuity of care difficult to achieve, something that is made harder still by changes to professional working patterns, larger practice sizes and division of services and out-of-hours care (Freeman and Hughes 2010). It is difficult to objectively measure continuity to evaluate improvement or decline, but measures of patient experience, such as the GP patient survey, provide some insights. Results from the past three years show a decline in the proportion of respondents reporting that they see or speak to their preferred GP 'always' or 'almost always', or 'a lot of the time' (from 65.3 per cent in June 2012 to 59.6 per cent in July 2015) (Ipsos MORI 2016).

Evidence from the literature as well as our case study sites suggests that continuity is highly valued by patients and health care professionals alike, particularly for people with chronic conditions, multi-morbidity and other complex health needs. Studies have found numerous benefits of continuity, including increased patient and staff satisfaction, greater accountability, increased trust within the doctor–patient relationship (with positive effects on treatment compliance), improved disease management and better health outcomes (Freeman and Hughes 2010). Loss of continuity is challenging for GPs as well as patients; it can be extremely difficult for a GP to understand and address the needs of a patient with complex problems within a single 10-minute consultation. The emphasis on rapid access over continuity can be a source of frustration for GPs, as one GP partner noted:

> I see a patient one week, order some tests... And I say, well, phone back or come and see me in two weeks and we'll discuss the next steps for a routine problem. Patients increasingly are phoning back the day after... Wanting to discuss their results with a colleague who isn't me who then might not be able to interpret them without knowing the full history. Our patient advisers are pretty good at saying 'Wouldn't it be better if you waited to speak to your doctor?'... 'No, no, I want to know now'... It's that 'now, now, now' culture, which I think is probably encouraged a bit by the media and by politicians.

A further concern expressed was that while other services were raising referral thresholds – mental health and district nursing services being the two most commonly mentioned – GPs were left managing difficult cases without support, and holding a level of risk that was adding to feelings of burnout.

The nature of general practice means that, while relationships within the primary care team may be good, it is an isolated occupation for clinicians. Unlike in a hospital setting – where there is a team of consultants, junior doctors, nursing and other staff all sharing the care of a patient – that sense of a team approach is much less evident in primary care. GPs do not have another doctor to hand over to at the end of a shift. Practice nurses have their own clearly defined work, and while we saw very good examples of administrative support in general practice, much of the burden of following up complex patients fell to the GP. One GP trainee illustrated this by saying:

> *What keeps me awake when I'm not in the surgery is 'Did that blood test come back showing high potassium levels and is it sitting unreviewed on my desk?' or 'Did that two-week breast cancer referral actually arrive and has the patient been seen?'*

Where people with chronic and complex conditions were receiving services from a wider health care team (for example, community matrons or district nurses), these appear to be mainly managed at arm's length from the GP. We heard some examples of GPs becoming involved in integrated care but this was usually not located within their practice.

A 2010 report by The King's Fund distinguishes between 'relationship continuity' (defined as a continuous therapeutic relationship with a clinician) and 'management continuity' (consistency of clinical management through care planning, co-ordination, effective handover, communication and information sharing) (Freeman and Hughes 2010). Successful team approaches to primary care have been developed in other countries. In Southcentral Foundation Alaska (Collins 2015), for example, each primary care team typically has one GP, one nurse case manager, one member of case management support staff and one certified medical assistant, responsible for around 1,400 people (a similar, if slightly smaller, population for GPs in England). Each group of six primary care teams also has support from a dietician, pharmacist, midwifery and behavioural health consultant, which is significantly more support than typically exists in English general practice. The same team approach has been adopted by Group Health in the United States, focusing not just on developing new roles but also allowing teams sufficient time to communicate and interact. In these systems, all members of the team operate at the 'top of their licence', yet the support structure offered by a well-resourced team seems to prevent feelings of burnout.

We found that the isolated nature of general practice and the rise in the intensity of work has also led to significant concerns about the ability to practice safely, as these comments from two GPs highlight:

> *Clinical work isn't the problem. It's having the capacity to do it safely. And I think the increasing complexity takes more time. You know, we've got more drug choices than we've ever had. We've got more complicated drugs than we've ever had. More complicated patients... The risk is much higher and yet we're dealing with more on a daily basis.*

> *But for some reason, the volume of contact is so vast... It has to give somewhere. And sometimes you deal with things far more superficially than you want to, just so you can go on to the next problem and the next problem. And there just isn't room to breathe... I don't want this to sound like a moan about workload. We all work hard. Everybody works hard. But it's about that capacity for safety. And I'm just worried that... You know, this morning, I had 15 telephone calls on top of a full list of patients. And again, that's fine. Get through it. If I'd had four house visits as well, then there would have been no time at all to even have this conversation before starting this afternoon. And you can see me now, I'm surrounded by paperwork.*

Finally, a fear of litigation came across strongly in our survey of trainees, who pointed to higher indemnity costs, increased incidence of complaints or being sued, and shifting public views about doctors:

> *Some patients are now recording consultations on their phones.*
> GP trainee

This increased intensity is having a direct impact on the ability to recruit and retain doctors. One of the most striking findings from our survey of GP trainees was that only 11 per cent intended to pursue full-time clinical work in general practice five years after qualifying. The key reason cited for not intending to pursue full-time clinical work was the intensity of the working day (22 per cent). This was followed by family commitments (19 per cent), long working hours (17 per cent), volume of administrative work (14 per cent), work-related stress (11 per cent) and interest in other work (10 per cent). The following comments reflect these reasons:

> *Time pressures and workload have made it impossible to be a full-time GP for a protracted period of time without incurring costs to one's own personal health and wellbeing. To prevent burnout, I intend to spread my work into different areas to gain more job satisfaction and better work–life balance.*

> *I'd like to work full-time but in the current climate I feel it might be detrimental to my physical and mental health as well as family life.*

> *The relentless pace of working days in general practice make me feel that I need some variety – I do not feel that I would be able to practice in a caring and effective manner if I worked 10 clinical sessions a week.*

> *I would like to work in general practice alongside other interests and hope to retain enthusiasm that way.*

> *I believe that general practice offers some of the greatest flexibility in medicine career-wise and people are taking advantage of that by working part-time, having a portfolio career and developing other interests. I think that this is also driven by the high pressure and current workload, which means that full-time clinical work alone is not sustainable for many and it helps to have other interests/roles.*

This was echoed by the more senior partners we spoke to across our case study sites:

> *I literally will go from the point of starting one session to the point of starting the next session and not have had time to do my admin… I have to then go home and it's not until I put my children to bed at night that I go back and I do my typical admin. So that's, you know, clinical letters, writing any reports, writing any sort of referral letters and, so, if I couldn't dial in to my practice mail – which it has been liberating to be able to do that and the IT being so important – I would be… I would feel very, very anxious because I would have to be leaving a lot of work undone from week to week.*

You can't do a consultation in 10 minutes particularly if you want to be as holistic as possible, so in my surgery I was always running an hour late until a patient in a workshop that I went to told me off for expecting people to wait an hour to see me, even if they really wanted to see me. And, I thought he's so right. So, I've now accepted that I will always take more time and so, I still run… We actually run 12-minute appointments here, but, I still book a 12-minute appointment, but put buffers all the way through, so my appointments are now 15 minutes. My patients don't actually know that, but, it is 15 minutes, and that's enabled me to run to time and to ensure that people are getting the time that I was giving them anyway and that they need, and that's taken some of the stress off me… A four-hour [session] of mine is now all face-to-face and I do my admin at home.

It's a really stressful job all the time thinking, have I done enough? Have I done the right thing? Have I really considered that diagnosis? Have I considered all the other possible diagnoses? Have I missed something? Is that cough something else completely? Not trying to just pattern recognise but actually be aware for when it could be something else, whether the persistent cough could be a bacterial endocarditis or a pulmonary embolism or any one of other things or drug-related thing. So that there are lots of issues with that and admitting patients to hospital takes so long now that you, kind of, do during the surgery almost anything rather than have to go through the admissions service because it takes so long.

Studies from other countries have also reported burnout in doctors in primary care as a result of a narrow focus on increasing productivity. Group Health in the United States implemented reforms to improve the productivity of primary care in the early 2000s, including advanced access, shorter visits and leaner teams. It found that while productivity improved, so did burnout. When they implemented a re-designed model of care with longer appointment times and larger teams, the results included improved patient experience, a reduction in burnout, improved clinical quality and even cost-effectiveness (Reid *et al* 2010). The Buurtzorg model of district nursing, developed in the Netherlands (in which highly trained nurses carry out all of a patient's care) has also seen excellent results in terms of both quality and cost (Gray *et al* 2015).

GPs are reporting high levels of stress and burnout. A recent Commonwealth Fund survey of GPs across 11 countries found that GPs in the United Kingdom reported the highest levels of stress, with 59 per cent reporting that their job was 'extremely stressful' or 'very stressful', compared to 18 per cent in the Netherlands and an average of 35 per cent across all 11 countries (Osborn and Schneider 2015). Other studies and surveys have echoed this sense of burnout (Doran *et al* 2016). The *Eighth national GP worklife survey* published in 2015 reported the lowest levels of job satisfaction among GPs since before the introduction of their new contract in 2004, the highest levels of stress since the start of the survey series in 1998, and more GPs intending to quit direct patient care within the next five years than was the case just three years ago (Gibson *et al* 2015). The proportion of respondents reporting that they 'have to work very intensively' was 95 per cent, with 89 per cent reporting that they 'have to work very fast'. Fewer than 10 per cent of respondents thought that 'recent changes to their job had led to better patient care' (Gibson *et al* 2015).

8 Prescription for the future?

The increasing demands on general practice have not been accompanied by a commensurate increase in capacity. The significant growth in the workload, compounded by the increasing complexity and intensity of that work, has led to workforce challenges, notably in recruiting and retaining GPs who want to do full-time, patient-facing clinical work. Policies that have emphasised a transfer of care from secondary to primary and community settings have not been supported by a transfer of funding.

As the pressure on general practice has increased, the experience for patients has declined. Although satisfaction levels are still high, they have decreased and the proportion of patients describing their experience as 'poor' or 'very poor' has increased. At the same time, more people report difficulty in accessing care, are more likely to report that they were unable to get an appointment or to see someone the last time they tried, and are less satisfied with their experience of using GP services.

It is clear that the current situation is untenable if general practice is to remain at the heart of health care in England. The principles of general practice, providing entry to the health system and a 'medical home' for patients, will require a new approach – one that recognises that the current model is not fit for a population with increasing and multiple long-term conditions and that is funded in a way that adequately reflects increased demands on both primary and community care.

Based on our research, our 'prescription' for the future of general practice that can deliver the care people need has five items, which we explain in detail below: understanding data at a system level; improving the current system of care; developing and promoting new models of general practice; developing and sustaining a workforce for the future; and ensuring that capacity and funding match changing workloads.

Our prescription goes beyond restoring patients' confidence in getting appointments when they need them, and seeks to provide them with a better experience of the whole health and social care system. New models for general practice must enable delivery of integrated care for the increasing numbers of patients with chronic conditions. This means they will get care from co-ordinated teams of professionals from across the health and care spectrum, who plan that care together with patients and people in their support networks taking account of their personal needs. The measures we recommend for re-designing the commissioning framework, building new provider models, developing the workforce and ensuring investment in general practice keeps up with the demands placed on it are all designed to further this goal.

Understanding data at a system level

It is unacceptable for there to be an absence of data for secondary use about workload in general practice that can be collated and analysed and available to commissioners and policy-makers. Without an understanding of changes in activity and demand or supply, neither national policy-makers nor local commissioners can be sure whether general practice has capacity for patients to access care when they need it. The pressures in accident and emergency (A&E) services are immediately visible to commissioners and policy-makers through almost real-time data. It simply would not be acceptable if information about A&E was only available through retrospective research studies examining data which is at best a year after the fact. The development of data for secondary use in primary care, whether provided through the General Practice Extraction Service (GPES), care.data or other routes, is essential, though we acknowledge this will be challenging. It will also require the development of national standards for data entry to ensure that data is consistent and comparable across practices.

Improving the current system of care

There are already a wide range of initiatives – such as those included in NHS England's *General practice forward view* – under way to address some of the issues highlighted in this report, which will go some way to helping general practice manage its increasing (and increasingly complex) workload and make sure patients have access to high-quality care. All of these initiatives will require general practice to have access to quality and service improvement expertise and support. As a priority, the following issues need to be addressed.

Managing access

Patients want rapid access to general practice, and successive governments have made this a priority. Practices that have successfully managed to implement access schemes are better able to manage 'on-the-day' demand from patients and use of technology such as telephone and online triage can have significant impact though there is wide variation in implementation. General practice requires access to quality and service improvement expertise and support if it is to reduce variation in access.

General practice has developed a wide range of initiatives to successfully manage less serious illness, including nurse-led minor illness clinics and the use of other clinicians, including pharmacists and physiotherapists. It is likely that people will want both ease of access and effectiveness of care, and so any initiative to manage minor illness will need to deliver both. However, initiatives to access and manage minor illness will not address the growing intensity and complexity of the work.

Reducing bureaucratic burden and streamlining commissioning

The complex and piecemeal nature of funding for general practice places a significant burden on practice managers and GP partners. An adversarial approach to commissioning and contracting has resulted in a 'shopping list' of tasks required of GPs from commissioners and politicians, and a protectionist response from general practice, with a lack of trust on both sides and a sense that each side is being taken for granted. Any commissioning of new models of care will need to carefully consider how these models will be transacted and how money and risk will flow, as perverse consequences are likely to undermine effort.

Managing relationships with the wider system

Improving joint working between primary care and other parts of the health and care system will be critical to relieving unnecessary burden on general practice and delivering better co-ordinated care to patients. As a minimum, this means improving communication between general practice and hospitals. This will require investment in shared electronic records and may require the transactional flows to be examined to remove barriers and perverse incentives that prevent collaborative working. It may also require secondary care specialists to reach out to provide support to primary care (Robertson *et al* 2014). Issues in the relationship with secondary care are also being addressed through the BMA, RCGP, Academy of Medical Royal Colleges and others but to make sure these kind of relationships are the norm and not the happy exceptions, there must be quite fundamental changes to the incentive structure GPs and acute trusts operate under. There should be a renewed focus on building communication between general practice and community and mental health services.

Opportunities to use technology

There are opportunities to make better use of online access channels to general practice but they are under-developed and under-researched. The recent emphasis on online transactions is welcome, provided that practices receive support to develop their digital processes and improve the digital skills of the workforce.

Capitalising on community assets in general practice

General practice has a significant role to play in harnessing community assets to support the health and wellbeing of its registered population. One example is the Bromley by Bow Centre, which works in partnership with local GPs and community groups. Initiatives linked to general practice that have been shown to improve the health of local populations include social prescribing (Brandling and House 2009), advice services (Parkinson and Buttrick 2015) and community health champion schemes. National programmes based around health champions have shown benefits for patients and practices alike (Altogether Better Wellbeing 2 Programme 2015). The King's Fund is examining the scale, scope and value of volunteering in general practice, and is due to report the findings later in 2016 (The King's Fund 2016).

These short-term measures should help to give confidence that the crisis in general practice is recognised and will be addressed, and build towards longer-term solutions.

New models of general practice

While the initiatives mentioned above are aimed at helping practices become more effective and efficient, we think that the health system will need to make more radical changes if primary care is going to effectively remain at its heart. The focus should be on developing new organisational forms, implementing integrated care, and ensuring continuity of care through greater teamworking, so that patients receive both timely access to care and continuity where it matters to them.

Integrated care

Demographic changes mean that the task of general practice is now, overwhelmingly, to provide ongoing clinical management of people with long-term chronic conditions; the locus of care for that population has shifted into primary care. The loss of generalist physicians in secondary care has increased the need for GPs to co-ordinate the care of patients with multi-morbidities. Given this changed context, having arm's length relationships with other teams also managing this population does not make sense.

For patients with long-term and chronic conditions, these arm's length relationships are at best inconvenient to patients and at worst harmful to the quality of the care. General practice, with its model of a registered list and (often) named GP, is an obvious place to locate the co-ordination and integration of care. Yet because of the variety and sheer number of practices, together with an increasingly demanding workload, one of the biggest challenges integrated care programmes have faced across the country has been engaging with 'primary care as provider'.

The result is that these programmes struggle to put general practice at their heart. The new model for general practice must enable GPs or their team members to take on the task of co-ordinating care for their population, by providing them with the right resources in terms of time, money, skill-mix and (crucially) closer working relationships with secondary and community care teams.

Delivering continuity of care through teamworking

Continuity of care is fundamental to effective primary care and is highly valued by patients, particularly those with chronic, multiple and complex needs. It is also valued by primary care professionals, and is a motivating factor for working in general practice. As the current general practice model makes it difficult to achieve relationship continuity, robust systems to support and co-ordinate management continuity are key. Models of general practice, and appointment systems in particular, should facilitate and support continuity rather than neglecting it in the drive for ever more rapid access, important as access is for many patients.

Policy-makers need to be realistic about what continuity means in contemporary general practice and how best to support this. If 'named GPs' are to be accountable for the co-ordination and delivery of a patient's care they will require a practice team who collaborate around a patient and robust processes, tools and ways of working as teams to effectively manage a panel of patients. Learning from systems such as the Southcentral and Group Health models in the United States will be important.

General practice at scale

How might the traditional partnership model of general practice need to change to enable this kind of care to be delivered to patients? The national trend has been towards larger practices, and successive governments have instigated policies to promote these. Primary care federations give practices the opportunity to retain their individual structures but come together to deliver an enhanced range of services and can achieve the advantages of scale, such as more diverse skills in the team and greater capacity to manage the relationships and contracts with other providers important for integrated care.

Large single-partnership practices operating across multiple sites in an area can also provide economies of scale and offer better access to development opportunities for clinical and management staff. Regional multipractice organisations such as Modality in Birmingham can also provide advantages such as shared leadership, shared back-office support and workforce development and can offer different career structures. The ability to extend scale and scope must be balanced with maintaining continuity for patients and the autonomy in professional practice that has been at the heart of the partnership model. It is particularly important that the discretionary effort GPs have traditionally put into running practices they own is not lost.

New models of care

Through the new care model vanguard programme, general practice now has the opportunity to drive the development of new provider forms. Primary and acute care systems (PACS) and multispecialty community providers (MCPs) are the two models covering primary care. We have previously argued that GP practices' possession of registered lists of patients means they must play a central role in developing such models (Addicott and Ham 2014). If funding for general practice is brought together with the funding for community care, social care and other services it could improve health and social care outcomes for local populations and be responsive to what local people need and want.

In general, the approach to commissioning and contracting general practice, and indeed the wider system, needs to move away from over-specification of individual actions and services and move towards an approach that commissions and contracts for outcomes the local population, rewards integrated care and enables resources to be re-invested and deployed outside acute settings. The government's announcement of an optional new contract available to larger practices or federations may help to facilitate this.

Principles for designing new models

The financial problems facing the secondary care sector are clearly visible and have been the driving force behind many recent policy initiatives. The lack of data about workload in general practice has meant that the effects of the current financial pressures and changes in health policy are largely invisible. Deficits in general practice do not show up on the NHS's balance sheet; rather they are absorbed by GPs taking pay cuts and spreading staff more thinly.

The voice of GPs as providers of care is also largely absent at the system level. When GPs participate in system planning as leaders of clinical commissioning groups they are there as commissioners –and in fact are actively discouraged from being the voice of the provider as that would be a conflict of interest. Local medical committees (LMCs) may provide one route to a provider voice, as will larger groups of GPs working at scale, but even so it will be hard for GPs to act as provider at a system level.

Any reformed system must have general practice at its heart, and that will require system leaders to gain a much better understanding of the potential impact of reform on general practice.

Developing and sustaining a workforce for the future

Whatever the model of delivery, general practice requires an adequate, skilled and motivated workforce. If the policy objective to recruit and retain 5,000 more GPs by 2020 is to be achievable, more needs to be done to ensure that general practice is an attractive and sustainable career option.

Supporting sustainable careers in general practice

Our research found that many in general practice felt their jobs were neither possible to fulfil nor fulfilling. While some initiatives have been instigated to enhance recruitment, retention and return to general practice (NHS England *et al* 2015) we believe further reform is needed. Future workforce planning needs to take into account the fact that most GPs will not be delivering full-time clinical care in general practice. The recent expansion on the GP role in leading, managing and indeed commissioning services will mean that even more GPs are needed to ensure enough capacity for clinical care. New models of provision, such as MCPs, may provide one route to a broader portfolio career. It will also be important to address the impact of the increasing intensity of work on the time GPs have for patient education, as well as time for pastoral care and support for their staff, particularly staff in training.

Other members of the general practice team need attractive and sustainable career options. The Primary Care Workforce Commission suggests a range of ways to enhance practice nurse recruitment including management and leadership skills and clear pathways for career progression (Primary Care Workforce Commission 2015).

There has not been the same investment in general management in primary care as there has in secondary care, and while larger practices may be able to recruit more managerial staff, practice managers on the whole remain isolated and unsupported. There should be greater efforts to support practice managers, particularly in accessing quality and service improvement skills.

Developing new clinical support roles

Our research also highlighted new roles that have been introduced to the primary care team, including pharmacists, paramedics, health care assistants, physician associates, health coaches and specialist nurses. All of these have the potential to alleviate part of the burden and intensity felt by GPs in managing patients with both acute and long-term conditions. A concerted effort to engage these professional groups might help to relieve pressure in the short term while also being consistent with the longer term direction of policy. It is important that any new models of workforce in primary care follow rather than precede a re-design of the work (Imison and Bohmer 2013), and that practices analyse the clinical needs of the population and their workload when deciding what skills are required (Primary Care Workforce Commission 2015).

Developing leadership skills

Securing the future of general practice will require strong clinical and managerial leadership, so GPs and the wider practice team need to be equipped with the necessary skills. The Luton Future GP Leaders Scheme, for example, seeks to develop these skills at an early career stage; it offers three-year salaried GP posts that, alongside clinical work, provide experience and mentoring in commissioning leadership or education leadership, as well as the opportunity to study for an executive MBA or MA in medical education (Darnton *et al* 2015).

We have already noted that the huge range of clinical leadership tasks already required of GPs takes them away from patient-facing clinical work. The demands of clinically led commissioning and the development of new organisational models will require experienced GPs to focus further on management tasks. Any capacity planning needs to take into account this wide range of roles, with general practice adequately supported to do the development work required.

Ensuring that capacity and funding match changing workload

Government and policy-makers must recognise that the increasing volume and complexity of work in general practice has not been matched by a commensurate increase in funding, nor has the division of funding between primary and secondary care been adjusted to reflect the changing nature of care. The latest funding announcement will increase general practice's share of funding by 2020/21 but this money will also need to be used to extend opening hours further across seven days. Adequate additional workforce will be essential to ensure capacity meets demand. Otherwise, it will run the risk of spreading an already stretched workforce across longer working hours, thus increasing the workforce challenges. If general practice is to remain at the heart of the NHS, it must have an adequate and stable funding stream for core services. NHS England should commit to reporting on progress towards matching capacity and funding to demand based on new monitoring systems that can provide real-time analysis of activity and demand.

References

Addicott R, Ham C (2014). *Commissioning and funding general practice: making the case for family care networks*. London: The King's Fund. Available at: www.kingsfund.org.uk/publications/commissioning-and-funding-general-practice (accessed on 1 April 2016).

Addicott R, Maguire D, Honeyman M, Jabbal J (2015). *Workforce planning in the NHS*. London: The King's Fund. Available at: www.kingsfund.org.uk/publications/workforce-planning-nhs (accessed on 26 February 2016).

Altogether Better Wellbeing 2 Programme (2015). *Altogether better working together to create healthier people and communities: bringing citizens and services together in new conversations* [online]. Available at: www.altogetherbetter.org.uk/altogether-better-working-together-to-create-healthier-people-and-communities-bringing-citizens-and-services-together-in-new-conversations--the-evaluation-report-of-the-altogether-better-wellbeing-2-programme (accessed on 30 March 2016).

Appleby J, Robertson R (2016). *Public satisfaction with the NHS in 2015*. London: The King's Fund. Available at: www.kingsfund.org.uk/projects/public-satisfaction-nhs/bsa-survey-2015 (accessed on 23 March 2016).

Appleby J, Robertson R (2015). *Public satisfaction with the NHS in 2014*. London: The King's Fund. Available at: www.kingsfund.org.uk/projects/public-satisfaction-nhs/bsa-survey-2014 (accessed on 5 April 2016).

Banks I (2010). 'Self care of minor ailments: a survey of consumer and healthcare professional beliefs and behaviour'. *SelfCare*, vol 1, pp 1–13.

Barnett K, Mercer SW, Norbury M, Watt G, Wyke S, Guthrie B (2012). 'Epidemiology of multimorbidity and implications for health care, research, and medical education: a cross-sectional study'. *The Lancet*, vol 380, no 9836, pp 37–43.

Boomla K, Hull S, Robson J (2014). 'GP funding formula masks major inequalities for practices in deprived areas'. *The BMJ*, vol 349, g7648.

Bounds A, Neville S (2015). 'GPs threaten protests over cuts that could hit 40% of surgeries'. *Financial Times*, 11 November.

Boyle S, Appleby J, Harrison A (2010). *A rapid review of access to care: an inquiry into the quality of General Practice in England*. London: The King's Fund. Available at: www.kingsfund.org.uk/projects/gp-inquiry/access-to-care (accessed on 5 April 2016).

Bradby M, McCallum C (2015). *General practice nursing in the 21st century: a time of opportunity.* London: The Queen's Nursing Institute. Available at: www.qni.org.uk/for_nurses/publications (accessed on 29 February 2016).

Brandling J, House W (2009). 'Social prescribing in general practice: adding meaning to medicine'. *British Journal of General Practice*, vol 59, no 563, pp 454–6.

Campbell J, Fletcher E, Britten N, Green C, Holt T, Lattimer V, Richards DA, Richards SH, Salisbury C, Calitri R, Boywer V, Chaplin K, Kandiyali R, Murdoch J, Roscoe J, Varley A, Warren FC, Taylor RS (2014). 'Telephone triage for management of same-day consultation requests in general practice (the ESTEEM trial): a cluster-randomised controlled trial and cost-consequence analysis'. *The Lancet*, vol 384, no 9957, pp 1859–68.

Campbell SM, Kontopantelis E, Reeves D, Valderas JM, Gaehl E, Small N, Roland MO (2010). 'Changes in patient experiences of primary care during health service reforms in England between 2003 and 2007'. *Annals of Family Medicine*, vol 8, no 6, pp 499–506.

Cancer Research UK (2014). *Be Clear on Cancer evaluation update.* London: Cancer Research UK. Available at: www.cancerresearchuk.org/health-professional/early-diagnosis-activities/be-clear-on-cancer/programme-evaluation (accessed on 26 February 2016).

Clay H, Stern R (2015). *Making time in general practice: freeing GP capacity by reducing bureaucracy and avoidable consultations, managing the interface with hospitals and exploring new ways of working.* London: NHS Alliance and Primary Care Foundation. Available at: www.nhsalliance.org/mediacentre/making-time-in-general-practice/ (accessed on 13 April 2016).

Collins B (2015). *Intentional whole health system redesign: Southcentral Foundation's 'Nuka' system of care.* London: The King's Fund. Available at: www.kingsfund.org.uk/publications/commissioned/intentional-whole-health-system-redesign-nuka-southcentral (accessed on 1 April 2016).

Curry N (2015). *Fact or fiction? Demand for GP appointments is driving the 'crisis' in general practice.* London: Nuffield Trust. Available at: www.nuffieldtrust.org.uk/blog/fact-or-fiction-demand-gp-appointments-driving-crisis-general-practice (accessed on 5 April 2016).

Darnton R, Pearson N, Morris C, Preston-Shoot M (2015). 'Where will our future GP leaders come from?' *BMJ Careers*, 24 March. Available at: http://careers.bmj.com/careers/advice/Where_will_our_future_GP_leaders_come_from%3F (accessed on 30 March 2016).

Deloitte (2014). *Under pressure: the funding of patient care in general practice.* London: Deloitte. Available at: www.rcgp.org.uk/campaignhome/~/media/Files/PPF/Deloitte%20Report_Under%20Pressure.ashx (accessed on 19 April 2016).

Department of Health (2015). *Department of Health annual report and accounts 2014–15* [online]. Gov.uk website. Available at: www.gov.uk/government/publications/department-of-health-annual-report-and-accounts-2014-to-2015 (accessed on 6 April 2016).

Department of Health (2014). *Department of Health annual report and accounts 2013–14* [online]. Gov.uk website. Available at: www.gov.uk/government/publications/department-of-health-annual-report-and-accounts-2013-to-2014 (accessed on 21 April 2016).

Department of Health (2013). *Department of Health annual report and accounts 2012–13* [online]. Gov.uk website. Available at: www.gov.uk/government/publications/department-of-health-annual-report-and-accounts-2012-to-2013 (accessed on 21 April 2016).

Department of Health (2012a). *Department of Health annual report and accounts 2011–12* [online]. Gov.uk website. Available at: www.gov.uk/government/publications/department-of-health-annual-report-and-accounts-for-2011-to-2012-published (accessed on 21 April 2016).

Department of Health (2012b). *Long term conditions compendium of information: third edition.* Leeds: Department of Health. Available at: www.gov.uk/government/publications/long-term-conditions-compendium-of-information-third-edition (accessed on 29 March 2016).

Department of Health (2012c). *Report on the effect of the NHS Constitution.* London: Department of Health. Available at: www.gov.uk/government/publications/report-on-the-effect-of-the-nhs-constitution (accessed on 13 April 2016).

Department of Health (2011). *Department of Health annual report and accounts 2010–11* [online]. Gov.uk website. Available at: www.gov.uk/government/publications/department-of-health-annual-report-and-accounts-2010-11 (accessed on 21 April 2016).

Doran N, Fox F, Rodham K, Taylor G, Harris M (2016). 'Lost to the NHS: a mixed methods study of why GPs leave practice early in England'. *British Journal of General Practice*, vol 66, no 643, e128–34.

Foot C, Sonola L, Bennett L, Fitzsimons B, Raleigh V, Gregory S (2014). *Managing quality in community health care services.* London: The King's Fund. Available at: www.kingsfund.org.uk/publications/managing-quality-community-health-care-services (accessed on 30 March 2016).

Freeman G, Hughes J (2010). *Continuity of care and the patient experience.* Paper commissioned by The King's Fund to inform the Inquiry into the Quality of General Practice in England. London: The King's Fund. Available at: www.kingsfund.org.uk/projects/gp-inquiry/continuity-of-care (accessed on 13 April 2016).

Gibson J, Checkland K, Coleman A, Hann M, McCall R, Spooner S, Sutton M (2015). *Eighth national GP worklife survey.* Manchester: Policy Research Unit in Commissioning and the Healthcare System (PRUComm). Available at: www.population-health.manchester.ac.uk/healtheconomics/research/Reports/EighthNationalGPWorklifeSurveyreport/ (accessed on 30 March 2016).

Gilburt H (2015). *Mental health under pressure*. London: The King's Fund. Available at: www.kingsfund.org.uk/publications/mental-health-under-pressure (accessed on 30 March 2016).

Gray BH, Sarnak DO, Burgers JS (2015). *Home care by self-governing nursing teams: the Netherlands' Buurtzorg model*. New York: The Commonwealth Fund. Available at: www.commonwealthfund.org/publications/case-studies/2015/may/home-care-nursing-teams-netherlands (accessed on 29 February 2016).

Gulliford M, Latinovic R, Charlton J, Little P, van Staa T, Ashworth M (2009). 'Selective decrease in consultations and antibiotic prescribing for acute respiratory tract infections in UK primary care up to 2006'. *Journal of Public Health*, vol 31, no 4, pp 512–20. Available at: http://jpubhealth.oxfordjournals.org/content/31/4/512?ijkey=dd815b9020f2a4af0082924a589d61a2267c68d0&keytype2=tf_ipsecsha (accessed on 30 March 2016).

Health and Social Care Information Centre (HSCIC) (2015a). *General and personal medical services, England – 2004–2014 as at 30 September*. Leeds: Health & Social Care Information Centre. Available at: www.hscic.gov.uk/catalogue/PUB16934 (accessed on 29 February 2016).

Health and Social Care Information Centre (HSCIC) (2015b). *GP earnings and expenses 2013/14*. Leeds: Health & Social Care Information Centre. Available at: www.hscic.gov.uk/catalogue/PUB18375 (accessed on 13 April 2016).

Health and Social Care Information Centre (HSCIC) (2015c). *Hospital Episode Statistics. Hospital outpatient activity – 2014–15*. Leeds: Health & Social Care Information Centre. Available at: www.hscic.gov.uk/catalogue/PUB19608 (accessed on 5 April 2016).

Health and Social Care Information Centre (HSCIC) (2015d). *Hospital outpatient activity 2014/15*. Leeds: Health and Social Care Information Centre. Available at: www.hscic.gov.uk/catalogue/PUB19608 (accessed on 21 April 2016).

Health and Social Care Information Centre (HSCIC) (2015e). *Investment in general practice, 2010–11 to 2014–15, England, Wales, Northern Ireland and Scotland*. Leeds: Health & Social Care Information Centre. Available at: www.hscic.gov.uk/catalogue/PUB18469 (accessed on 30 March 2016).

Health and Social Care Information Centre (HSCIC) (2007). 2006/07 *UK General Practice Workload Survey*. Leeds: Health & Social Care Information Centre. Available at: www.hscic.gov.uk/pubs/gpworkload (accessed on 5 April 2016).

Healthwatch (2015). *A review of local Healthwatch reports* [online]. Available at: www.healthwatch.co.uk/resource/primary-care-review-local-healthwatch-reports (accessed on 1 April 2016).

Hibbard J, Gilburt H (2014). *Supporting people to manage their health: an introduction to patient activation*. London: The King's Fund. Available at www.kingsfund.org.uk/publications/supporting-people-manage-their-health (accessed on 30 March 2016).

Hobbs F, Bankhead C, Mukhtar T, Stevens S, Perera-Salazar R, Holt T, Salisbury C (2016). 'Clinical workload in UK primary care: a retrospective analysis of 100 million consultations in England, 2007–14'. *The Lancet*, 5 April online. Available at: www.thelancet.com/journals/lancet/article/PIIS0140-6736(16)00620-6/abstract (accessed on 13 April 2016).

Holder H, Robertson R, Naylor C, Ross S, Machaqueiro S (2016). *Has clinical commissioning found its voice? GP perspectives on their CCGs.* Slideset. London: The King's Fund and Nuffield Trust. Available at: www.kingsfund.org.uk/audio-video/gp-perspectives-ccg (accessed on 5 April 2016).

Imison C, Bohmer R (2013). *NHS and social care workforce: meeting our needs now and in the future?* London: The King's Fund. Available at: www.kingsfund.org.uk/time-to-think-differently/publications/nhs-and-social-care-workforce (accessed on 1 April 2016).

Imison C, Naylor C (2010). *Referral management: lessons for success.* London: The King's Fund. Available at: www.kingsfund.org.uk/publications/referral-management (accessed on 30 March 2016).

Ipsos MORI (2016). *GP Patient Survey – National summary report.* Leeds: NHS England, Ipsos MORI Social Research Institute. Available at: https://gp-patient.co.uk/surveys-and-reports#jan-2016 (accessed on 5 April 2016).

Laurant M, Reeves D, Hermens R, Braspenning J, Grol R, Sibbald B (2005). 'Substitution of doctors by nurses in primary care (Cochrane Review)'. *Cochrane Database of Systematic Reviews*, issue 18, article CD001271.

Lind S, Mooney H (2013). 'Demotivated practice managers consider new career as vacancies rise 12%'. *Pulse*, 14 October. Available at: www.pulsetoday.co.uk/your-practice/practice-topics/employment/demotivated-practice-managers-consider-new-career-as-vacancies-rise-12/20004721.fullarticle (accessed on 30 March 2016).

Longman H, Laitner S (2013). 'A disruptive innovation in general practice'. Presentation to The King's Fund, 19 June. Available at: www.kingsfund.org.uk/sites/files/kf/media/harry-longman-steve-laitner-transforming-general-practice-kingsfund-jun13.pdf (accessed on 30 March 2016).

Martin F, Thorpe T, Heath H, Noble H (2011). *Quest for quality. An inquiry into the quality of healthcare support for older people in care homes: a call for leadership, partnership and improvement.* London: British Geriatrics Society. Available at: www.bgs.org.uk/index.php?option=com_content&view=article&id=1487&Itemid=719 (accessed on 29 February 2016).

Mental Health Taskforce (2016). *The five year forward view for mental health.* Leeds: NHS England. Available at: www.england.nhs.uk/mentalhealth/taskforce/ (accessed on 13 April).

National Audit Office (2015). *Stocktake of access to general practice in England.* HC 605 Session 2015–16, 27 November 2015. London: House of Commons.

Naylor C, Das P, Ross S, Honeyman M, Thompson J, Gilburt H (2016). *Bringing together physical and mental health: a new frontier for integrated care*. London: The King's Fund. Available at: www.kingsfund.org.uk/publications/physical-and-mental-health (accessed on 30 March 2016).

Naylor C, Parsonage M, McDaid D, Knapp M, Fossey M, Galea A (2012). *Long-term conditions and mental health: the cost of co-morbidities*. London: The King's Fund and Centre for Mental Health. Available at: www.kingsfund.org.uk/publications/long-term-conditions-and-mental-health (accessed on 30 March 2016).

Nelson P, Murray J, Kahn MS (2010). *NHS Choices primary care consultation final report 2010*. London: Imperial College London. Available at: www.nhs.uk/aboutNHSChoices/professionals/developments/Documents/annual-report/primary-care-consultation-report.pdf (accessed on 30 March 2016).

NHS Employers (2015). *2015/16 General Medical Services (GMS) contract Quality and Outcomes Framework (QOF)*. London: NHS Employers. Available at: www.nhsemployers.org/your-workforce/primary-care-contacts/general-medical-services/quality-and-outcomes-framework (accessed on 18 April 2016).

NHS Employers (2014). 'Changes to QOF 2014/15'. London: NHS Employers. Available at: www.nhsemployers.org/your-workforce/primary-care-contacts/general-medical-services/quality-and-outcomes-framework/changes-to-qof-201415 (accessed on 29 February 2016).

NHS England (2016a). 'Cancer waiting times. National time series Q4 2008–09 to Q3 2015–16 (provider based)'. NHS England website. Available at: www.england.nhs.uk/statistics/statistical-work-areas/cancer-waiting-times/ (accessed on 6 April 2015).

NHS England (2016b). *General practice forward view*. London: NHS England. Available at: www.england.nhs.uk/ourwork/gpfv/ (accessed on 21 April 2016).

NHS England (2015). 'About wave two pilots'. NHS England website. Available at: www.england.nhs.uk/ourwork/futurenhs/pm-ext-access/wave-two/about-wave-two-pilots/ (accessed on 6 April 2016).

NHS England, Health Education England, Royal College of General Practitioners, British Medical Association (2015). 'Building the workforce – the new deal for general practice'. Leeds: NHS England. Available at: www.england.nhs.uk/commissioning/primary-care-comm/gp-action-plan/ (accessed on 13 April 2016).

NICE (2015). *Suspected cancer: recognition and referral*. London: National Institute for Health and Care Excellence. Available at: www.nice.org.uk/guidance/ng12 (accessed on 30 March 2016).

NICE (2011). *Hypertension in adults: diagnosis and management*. London: National Institute for Health and Care Excellence. Available at: www.nice.org.uk/guidance/CG127 (accessed on 30 March 2016).

Osborn R, Schneider E (2015). *International Health Policy Survey of Primary Care Physicians* [online]. The Commonwealth Fund. Available at: www.commonwealthfund.org/publications/in-the-literature/2015/dec/primary-care-physicians-in-ten-countries?utm_content=bufferf2ced&utm_medium=social&utm_source=twitter.com&utm_campaign=buffer (accessed on 5 April 2016).

Parkinson A, Buttrick J (2015). *The role of advice services in health outcomes: evidence review and mapping study* [online]. Advice Services Alliance. Available at: http://asauk.org.uk/the-role-of-advice-services-in-health-outcomes/ (accessed on 13 April 2016).

Porteous T, Ryan M, Bond CM, Hannaford P (2006). 'Preferences for self-care or professional advice for minor illness: a discrete choice experiment'. *British Journal of General Practice*, vol 56, no 533, pp 911–17. Available at: www.ncbi.nlm.nih.gov/pubmed/17132378 (accessed on 26 February 2016).

Primary Care Workforce Commission (2015). *The future of primary care: creating teams for tomorrow*. Leeds: Health Education England. Available at: www.hee.nhs.uk/our-work/hospitals-primary-community-care/primary-community-care/primary-care-workforce-commission (accessed on 29 February 2016).

Public Health England (2015). *Historical vaccine development and introduction of vaccines in the UK*. London: Public Health England. Available at: www.gov.uk/government/publications/vaccination-timeline (accessed on 29 February 2016).

Reid RJ, Coleman K, Johnson EA, Fishman PA, Hsu C, Soman MP, Trescott CE, Erikson M, Larson EB (2010). 'The Group Health medical home at year two: cost savings, higher patient satisfaction, and less burnout for providers'. *Health Affairs (Millwood)*, vol 29, no 5, pp 835–43.

Rennie L, Porteous T, Ryan M (2012). 'Preferences for managing symptoms of differing severity: a discrete choice experiment'. *Value in Health*, vol 15, no 8, pp 1069–76. Available at: www.sciencedirect.com/science/article/pii/S1098301512016531 (accessed on 29 February 2016).

Rimmer A (2015). 'A sixth of GP training places are unfilled after two recruitment rounds'. *BMJ Careers*, 13 August. Available at: http://careers.bmj.com/careers/advice/A_sixth_of_GP_training_places_are_unfilled_after_two_recruitment_rounds (accessed on 5 April 2016).

Robertson R, Sonola L, Honeyman M, Brooke B, Kothari S (2014). *Specialists in out-of-hospital settings: findings from six case studies*. London: The King's Fund. Available at: www.kingsfund.org.uk/publications/specialists-out-hospital-settings (accessed on 1 April 2016).

Rosen R (2014). *Meeting need or fuelling demand? Improved access to primary care and supply-induced demand*. London: Nuffield Trust. Available at: www.nuffieldtrust.org.uk/publications/meeting-need-or-fuelling-demand (accessed on 29 February 2016).

Salisbury C, Procter S, Stewart K, Bowen L, Purdy S, Ridd M, Valderas J, Blakeman T, Reeves D (2013). 'The content of general practice consultations: cross-sectional study based on video recordings'. *British Journal of General Practice*, vol 63, no 616, e751–9.

Shum C, Humphreys A, Wheeler D, Cochrane M-A, Skoda S, Clement S (2000). 'Nurse management of patients with minor illnesses in general practice: multicentre, randomised controlled trial'. *BMJ*, vol 320, no 7241, pp 1038–43.

The King's Fund (2016). 'Volunteering in general practice.' The King's Fund website. Available at: www.kingsfund.org.uk/projects/volunteering-general-practice (accessed on 1 April 2016).

About the authors

Beccy Baird has worked at The King's Fund since 2007, first as adviser to the chief executive and now as fellow in health policy, conducting research and analysis across a range of health care issues. Recent work includes projects on professional regulation, service transformation in mental health and an assessment of the NHS under the coalition government.

Beccy has a background in the NHS and social care, and before joining the Fund was Associate Director for Service Improvement at South East London Cancer Network. Prior to this she spent two years in San Mateo County, California, developing a model of integrated health and social care funding and delivery for older people. She began her career as a researcher and undertook a variety of roles in older people and mental health services, including a short secondment to the Department of Health to work on the development of the National Service Framework for Older People.

She has an MSc in Health Systems Management from the London School of Hygiene and Tropical Medicine.

Beccy is also a trustee of Young Minds, the national charity for children and young people's mental health.

Anna Charles joined The King's Fund's policy team in September 2015 as a research assistant. Her current projects include an evaluation of the sustainability of social care services and qualitative research into patient and staff experiences of community health services for older people.

Prior to joining the Fund, Anna worked as a doctor at Imperial College Healthcare NHS Trust, where she was awarded two deanery prizes for her clinical work. She also completed a number of quality improvement projects, including a large audit examining assessment of frail older patients before surgery, which was shortlisted for Junior Doctor Clinical Audit of the Year.

Anna is also interested in prison health care and related policy, and has published a number of research papers exploring contemporary issues in prison health care. She holds a medical degree and a BMedSc in Healthcare Ethics and Law from the University of Birmingham.

Matthew Honeyman joined The King's Fund's policy team in July 2013 as a researcher. Matthew's recent work includes projects on acute hospitals, specialist care in out-of-hospital settings, and commissioning for integrated care.

Matthew has a special interest in the relationship between health care, public policy and digital technology, and how the NHS adapts and adopts new innovations across the system. He is a member of the scientific committee for the Fund's annual Digital Health and Care Congress.

Previously, Matthew worked as a researcher and co-ordinator at the Innovation Unit on projects across health, education and local government. He has also worked as an intern at University College London's Constitution Unit, where he was part of a team researching the role of special advisers in the UK's political system and wrote a research note on special advisers in the Cabinet.

He holds a Philosophy, Politics and Economics degree from Oxford University.

David Maguire is a data analyst at The King's Fund. He has particular interest in the application of statistical and economic techniques to health and social care, as well as the implications of policy change for the care received by patients and clients. David is a health economics graduate from the University of York, with particular expertise in data analysis, statistical inference and quantitative analysis within health and care.

Before joining the Fund, David worked as a graduate intern with the South Eastern Health and Social Care Trust in Northern Ireland. He worked in several areas across an integrated care system and advised on health economics, as well as quantitative evaluation techniques for pilot public health and social care schemes. Previously, he worked with researchers at University College Dublin to establish the value for money generated by a nutritional intervention for pregnant women.

Preety Das is a GP registrar who joined The King's Fund as part of an innovative training post at Imperial College Healthcare NHS Trust. She is interested in mental health, maternal and child health, and patient experience.

Preety holds a Masters in Public Health from Harvard University, where she focused on maternal, child and mental health policy with community-based research. She has conducted research in Boston Children's Hospital, leading to many publications. She completed her junior doctor training in London, during which she received deanery prizes for leadership and peer representation. She undertook her medical training at the University of Cambridge.

Acknowledgements

We would like to thank all those who contributed to the project, particularly staff from the four case study sites who gave up their time to be interviewed, staff from the 43 practices who returned our workload survey and the 318 GP trainees who completed our online survey.

We are grateful to the Royal College of General Practitioners and the programme directors of the Vocational Training Schemes in England who helped us to recruit participants for our surveys and case studies.

We would also like to thank those who provided insightful reviews of drafts of the report, including Professor Chris Salisbury, Dr Mark Davies and Dr Jon Dickson and colleagues at The King's Fund, as well as other experts who provided valuable perspectives during the course of our research.

Finally, we are indebted to TPP and, in particular, Dr Chris Bates and Ankit Sharma from TPP and ResearchOne, for providing us with data and supporting us in our analysis.

Published by
The King's Fund
11–13 Cavendish Square
London W1G 0AN
Tel: 020 7307 2568
Fax: 020 7307 2801

Email:
publications@kingsfund.org.uk

www.kingsfund.org.uk

© The King's Fund 2016

First published 2016 by
The King's Fund

Charity registration number:
1126980

All rights reserved, including
the right of reproduction in
whole or in part in any form

ISBN: 978 1 909029 61 3

A catalogue record for this
publication is available from
the British Library

Edited by Kathryn O'Neill

Typeset by
Grasshopper Design Company

Printed in the UK by
The King's Fund

The King's Fund is an independent charity working to improve
health and care in England. We help to shape policy and
practice through research and analysis; develop individuals,
teams and organisations; promote understanding of the health
and social care system; and bring people together to learn,
share knowledge and debate. Our vision is that the best
possible care is available to all.

www.kingsfund.org.uk   @thekingsfund